Geography for Life Act

with Answer Key
by Robin Elisabeth Datel

(HOLT)

World Geography Today

HOLT, RINEHART AND WINSTON

A Harcourt Education Company

Austin · New York · Orlando · Atlanta · San Francisco · Boston · Dallas · Toronto · London

The Author

Robin Elisabeth Datel is an instructor in the Department of Geography at California State University, Sacramento. She received her B.A. from the University of California, Davis, and her M.A. and Ph.D. from the University of Minnesota, all in geography. She has written numerous articles on historic preservation and urban geography in the United States and Europe. She has also received grants from the American Association of University Women and the American Council of Learned Societies. Ms. Datel is a past president of the Association of Pacific Coast Geographers and has many years of experience teaching courses that introduce future K–12 teachers to geography.

Cover description: photograph of a tapestry from Nigeria

Cover credit: Betty Press/Woodfin Camp & Associates, Inc.

Printed in the United States of America

ISBN 0-03-065416-5

1 2 3 4 5 6 7 8 9 095 04 03 02 01

Contents

Geography for Life Activities

Name _____ Class _____ Date _____

National Geography Standard 1   **Two Geographic Grids**

The idea of using a grid to locate places on Earth's surface is an old one, dating back more than 2,000 years. Today, many different grid systems are used. Some grids, such as the one created by parallels of latitude and meridians of longitude, cover the entire globe and are widely used. Other grids have been developed by the mapping agencies of individual countries or states. Some maps, such as the topographic maps prepared by the United States Geological Survey (USGS), include markings for more than one grid system.

Knowing how to find locations using latitude and longitude will ease your future use of maps. This exercise also touches on properties of the globe and on map projections. Before beginning the activity, read what your textbook has to say about latitude and longitude and/or review the basics in class. Use a separate piece of paper to answer any questions posed below.

You Are the Geographer

1. On Figure 1a, carefully draw in and label the following parallels of latitude: 45°N, 15°S, the Tropic of Cancer, the Tropic of Capricorn, and the Arctic Circle.

2. On Figure 1b, carefully draw in and label the following meridians of longitude: 25°W, 15°E, 100°E, the Prime Meridian, and the International Date Line.

3. On Figure 1c, plot and number the following locations: 45°N, 75°W; 0°, 45°E; 85°N, 160°W; and 25°S, 10°E.

4. Plot the following locations of cities on Figure 2 (a world map using the Mercator projection). Then use a globe or atlas to find their names and write them on the map: 59°N, 18°E; 23°N, 82°W; 34°S, 151°E; and 1°S, 37°E.

5. What is the latitude and longitude of your school? If you moved south 30° and east 120° from your school what would be your new latitude and longitude? Show both the location of your school and of this second point on Figure 2.

6. If a plane cuts through the center of Earth, that plane's intersection with Earth's surface is a great circle. An arc of a great circle is the shortest distance between any two points on Earth's surface. Use a globe and piece of string to determine the great circle route between Dallas, Texas and Islamabad, Pakistan. List four cities, islands, or other geographic features that are spread out along or near this great circle route. Now plot the positions of Dallas, Islamabad, and these four locations on Figure 2. Connect the six points with a smooth, curving line and label it "great circle route." The problem with such a route is that it is constantly changing direction, making it virtually impossible to use for navigation. So what navigators did was to draw short straight lines connecting a sequence of points on the great circle route. Do this for the six points on your great circle route. On a Mercator projection, such straight lines are rhumb lines or lines of constant compass direction. A navigator could follow such a line from Point A to Point B, then change direction at B so as to reach Point C, and so on. The great circle route was approximated by this means.

How far is the great circle route from Dallas to Islamabad? Use your string to measure the distance between them and mark it on your string. Put one end of the string on the Prime Meridian at the Equator and determine the number of degrees of longitude from there to the mark you made on the string. Multiply that number by 69 (the number of miles in one degree of longitude at the equator).

7. If you measured the distance between Dallas and Islamabad along a straight line between them on a Mercator projection, you would not be measuring the shortest distance between them on a globe. This makes the general point that maps inevitably distort certain properties of the globe. Different projections distort different properties. The Mercator projection, while useful for navigation (which is what it was designed for), hugely distorts relative sizes.

The grid of latitude and longitude remains mostly on our maps and in our minds. There are other grids that have left their marks on the actual surface of Earth. Among these is the township grid of the U. S. Public Land Survey. In 1785 newly settled lands were surveyed using this system. A rectangular survey was selected for its relative ease of use. Much of the United States north of the Ohio River and west of the Mississippi River and some Southern states have been surveyed and subdivided by this method.

The township grid is based on selected east-west *base lines* and north-south *meridians*. You can see the locations of these and their names at the Bureau of Land Management's website (www.ca.blm.gov/cadastral/meridian.html). Townships, which are 6-mile by 6-mile units of land, are identified with respect to a particular base line and meridian. The location of the township marked "A" on Figure 3a is described as Township 5 West, Range 3 South. This township is 5 townships west of the given meridian and 3 townships south of the given base line. Its abbreviated address is T5W, R3S. Notice on Figure 3a that every four township tiers, adjustments are made to the township boundaries to account for the fact that meridians converge toward the poles. This results in the offsetting of range lines along what are called *standard parallels*.

Each township is subdivided into 36 sections of 1 square mile each. The sections are numbered 1 through 36 in a serpentine pattern starting with 1 in the northeastern-most corner and proceeding west, then south to the next row, then east, and so on, finishing with 36 in the southeasternmost corner. Fill in these numbers on Figure 3b.

Each section is further subdivided into smaller units using fractions (usually quarters) and the directions NE, NW, SE, and SW (N, S, E, and W for halves). For example, the location of letter "C" in Figure 3c is the N1/2 of the SW 1/4 of the SE1/4 of Section 22, T4E, R1N. A section is one square mile or 640 acres. One quarter-section or 160 acres was the size of a normal homestead acquired by settlers who earned title to it by living on and cultivating it. The letter "D" occupies a quarter section on Figure 3c.

Chapter 1, Geography for Life Activities, *continued*

8. On Figure 3a, complete the labeling of townships and ranges and label the first standard parallel south.

9. Identify locations E, F, G, and H using U.S. Public Land Survey designations.

10. Find USGS topographic maps (available on the Internet, on disk, and on paper from libraries and stores) that show evidence of the U.S. Public Land Survey. Discuss the evidence in class.

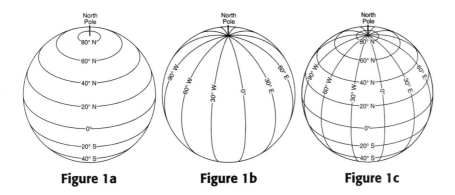

Figure 1a   **Figure 1b**   **Figure 1c**

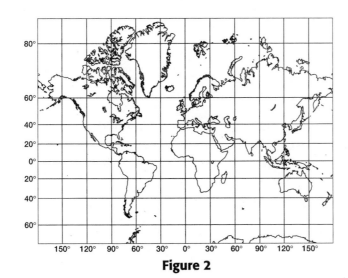

Figure 2

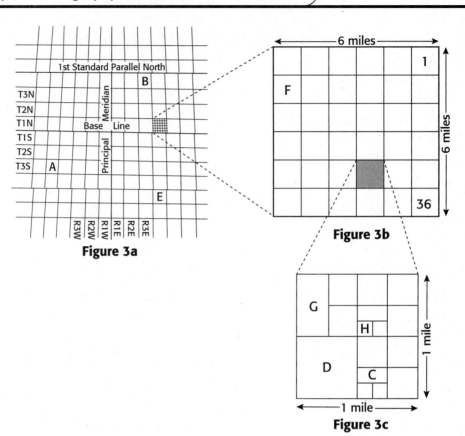

Figure 3a

Figure 3b

Figure 3c

Name _____ Class _____ Date _____

Geography for Life Activities

National Geography Standard 7

Hydrospheric Pursuit

The hydrosphere consists of Earth's water in all its forms. Included is surface water in oceans, lakes, rivers, and wetlands; underground water; and ice and snow in the atmosphere, on land and sea, or beneath Earth's surface. The hydrosphere includes water vapor and water droplets in the atmosphere. Water in the plants and animals that comprise the biosphere is simultaneously part of the hydrosphere. In this exercise you will become familiar with major geographic features of the hydrosphere. These include the oceans and ocean currents, major seas and bays, and selected lakes and river basins.

Currently, the oceans contain 97.2 percent of Earth's moisture. The remainder is divided as follows: glaciers, 2.0 percent; underground water, 0.5 percent; freshwater lakes, 0.1 percent; saline lakes, 0.1 percent; soil water, 0.4 percent; and stream, atmospheric, and biological water, 0.01 percent. During an ice age, these proportions change. The share of water in glaciers increases, while that in the oceans and the atmosphere decreases.

You Are the Geographer

Tables 1 through 4 on the following page list all the major geographic features of the hydrosphere. Locate and label them on the world outline map provided at the end of this activity. You will need to draw in the currents; use red pencil for the warm ones and blue for the cold. Also label Antarctica, Greenland, and the eastern Queen Elizabeth Islands with the words, "glacial ice." Label Antarctica's Ross Ice Shelf and Ronne Ice Shelf. Consult your textbook, atlases, wall maps, and/or globes to find the locations of all features.

Next, use your map, the tables on the following page, and other available reference works to prepare questions for a game of "hydrospheric pursuit." Use the blank page at the end of this activity to prepare your questions. Divide your class into teams and play. Below are some model questions.

1. Which one of the following river basins is not in South America?
   a. Lena   **b.** Paraná   **c.** Amazon

2. The Pacific Ocean is how many times larger than the Atlantic Ocean?
   a. 1.5 times   **b.** 2 times   **c.** 3 times

3. Which of the following currents is warm?
   a. California   **b.** Peru (Humboldt)   **c.** Kuroshio (Japan)

4. Besides the Yellow, Black, and Red, Earth has another sea named for a color. What is it?
   a. Blue Sea   **b.** Green Sea   **c.** White Sea

5. Which lake contains by far the most fresh water of any lake on Earth?
   a. Lake Malawi   **b.** Lake Baykal   **c.** Lake Huron

Name _____ Class _____ Date _____

Table 1. Marine Features of the Hydrosphere

Body of Water	Approximate Surface Area in Square Miles
Pacific Ocean	63,800,000
Atlantic Ocean	31,800,000
Indian Ocean	28,900,000
Arctic Ocean	5,400,000
Arabian Sea	1,492,000
South China Sea	1,150,000
Caribbean Sea	1,063,000
Mediterranean Sea	967,000
Bering Sea	876,000
Bay of Bengal	839,000
Gulf of Mexico	596,000
Sea of Okhotsk	550,000
East China Sea	480,000
Yellow Sea	480,000
Hudson Bay	475,000
Sea of Japan	389,000
North Sea	222,000
Black Sea	178,000
Red Sea	169,000
Baltic Sea	163,000

Table 2. Earth's Largest Lakes

Lake	Approximate Surface Area in Square Miles
Caspian Sea*	143,200
Lake Superior	31,700
Lake Victoria	26,800
Lake Huron	23,000
Lake Michigan	22,300
Aral Sea*	14,900
Lake Tanganyika	12,400
Lake Baykal	12,200
Great Bear Lake	12,096
Lake Malawi	11,200
Great Slave Lake	11,000
*Salt water.	

Table 3. Earth's 15 Largest Rivers

River	Approximate Drainage Area in Square Miles
Amazon	3,596,000
Congo (Zaire)	2,480,000
Nile	2,046,000
Mississippi	1,984,000
Yenisey	2,046,000
Lena	1,556,000
Ob'	1,550,000
Paraná	1,364,000
Chang	1,178,000
Niger	1,172,000
Amur	1,150,000
Mackenzie	1,141,000
Volga	843,000
Zambesi	825,000
St. Lawrence	806,000

Table 4. Major Surface Ocean Currents

North Pacific Ocean
- Alaska Current
- California Current
- Japan (Kuroshio) Current
- North Pacific Drift
- Oyashio (Kamchatka) Current

South Pacific Ocean
- Peru (Humboldt) Current
- East Australian Current

North Atlantic Ocean
- Canaries Current
- Gulf Stream and North Atlantic Drift
- Labrador Current

South Atlantic Ocean
- Benguela Current
- Brazil Current

Indian Ocean
- West Australian Current
- Agulhas Current

Multiple Oceans
- Equatorial Counter Current
- North Equatorial Current
- South Equatorial Current
- West Wind Drift

Note: Lakes are ranked by size of drainage basin.

Name _____ Class _____ Date _____

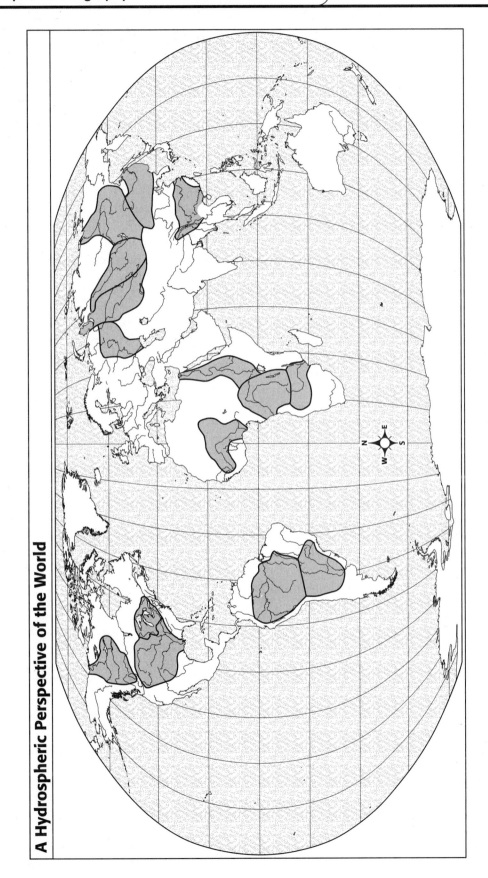

A Hydrospheric Perspective of the World

Hydrospheric Pursuit Questions

ACTIVITY 3   Geography for Life Activities
_____
National Geography Standard 18   **Global Climate Change**

> *Global climate change is one of the hottest research topics in science today.*
> *Many aspects of the environment and of human society are affected by climate.*
> *The possibility that it may be undergoing rapid change is cause for widespread*
> *concern. Scientists, policy makers, business leaders, and ordinary citizens want*
> *to know more about global climate change and what we can do about it.*

What evidence is there for global climate change? Temperature records (thermometer readings) indicate a warming of about 0.6°C in the average global surface temperature since 1861. This temperature change has lengthened the freeze-free season in many mid-latitude and high-latitude regions. We also have data on temperature changes in the lowest 8 kilometers of the atmosphere, starting in the 1950s. These records show an average increase in temperature of 0.1°C per decade.

Snow cover and ice extent have decreased. Satellite images show a 10 percent decrease in the extent of snow cover since the late 1960s in the middle and high latitudes of the northern hemisphere. Ground-based observations show a reduction of about two weeks in the annual duration of lake and river ice cover in the same region. Mountain glaciers in many non-polar regions retreated substantially during the 1900s. The extent and thickness of Northern Hemisphere sea ice have decreased, especially in the non-winter months.

Readings from tidal gauges show that the average global sea level rose between 10 and 20 centimeters during the 1900s. Subsurface temperature data, available since the 1950s, indicate increasing ocean heat content. As the upper layers of the ocean warm, water expands and sea level rises. Large-scale glacial melting also contributes to the rising sea level.

During the 1900s, some other changes occurred in the global climate. These changes include altered precipitation patterns and increases in cloud cover in some regions. Warm episodes of the El Niño-Southern Oscillation (ENSO) phenomenon have become more frequent, lengthy, and intense since the mid-1970s, compared with the previous 100 years. The ENSO phenomenon affects patterns of precipitation and temperature over much of the tropics, subtropics, and some mid-latitude areas.

Factors in Global Climate Change

Given that global warming has occurred, how do we explain it? More specifically, is it being caused by natural factors alone or are human beings contributing to it? Earth's climate has changed many times in the past. A large and complex body of evidence supports this assertion. Landforms, fossils, tree rings, coral, ice caps, and ocean and lake sediments preserve information about past climates. From such evidence we know, for example, about the alternating glacial (cold) and interglacial (warm) stages of the Pleistocene epoch. The last glacial stage of that epoch ended just 11,000 years ago. In studying climate change during historical times, researchers also make use of many kinds of documents. Even paintings can provide evidence of climate change. Rivers that today remain unfrozen are shown supporting ice skaters during the Northern Hemisphere's "Little Ice Age" from the 1400s to the 1800s.

To explain such earlier instances of climate change, scientists point to several natural phenomena. The total amount of solar energy Earth receives from the Sun and its geographic distribution is not constant. These variations are due to several factors. The tilt of Earth's axis varies. The path of Earth's orbit around the Sun varies; sometimes it is more circular, sometimes it is more elliptical in shape. Earth is nearest to the Sun at different times of year (for example, sometimes in the Northern Hemisphere's winter, sometimes in its summer). Temperatures at Earth's surface respond to these changes in Earth-Sun relationships.

Temperatures at Earth's surface also respond to the presence of aerosols in the atmosphere. These aerosols are fine solid or liquid particles. Large volcanic eruptions put vast quantities of particles into the atmosphere. These particles reflect some of the incoming solar radiation and cause cooling. A major meteorite impact that kicked up vast amounts of dust would have the same effect. Global climate change may also be affected by continental drift. Naturally occurring changes in greenhouse gases (see below) may also have contributed to climate change in the past. There is also a certain amount of variability within the climate system itself. In other words, some variability cannot be linked to any outside cause.

Many scientists have come to the conclusion that the above-named natural causes of global climate change cannot explain the magnitude and speed of the global warming now being experienced. Their computer models suggest that something else must be happening. The likely culprit is not hard to find.

Greenhouse Gases

Certain gases in the atmosphere are termed "greenhouse gases." This term is used because they act like the glass in a greenhouse. Incoming solar radiation (light) passes through them, but outgoing terrestrial radiation (heat) is trapped. The main greenhouse gases are water vapor, carbon dioxide, methane, nitrous oxide, and the chorofluorocarbons (CFCs). All of these gases except CFCs occur naturally. Together they make up less than one percent of the atmosphere. But this one percent of gases is enough to keep the planet 30°C warmer than it would otherwise be—a situation essential for life as we know it.

The levels of all these greenhouse gases, with the possible exception of water vapor, are rising due to human activity. The atmospheric concentration of carbon dioxide (CO_2) has increased 31 percent since 1750. This level of concentration has not been this high in the past half million years and likely not during the past 20 million years. Emissions of CO_2 come mainly from burning coal, oil, and natural gas. Deforestation is also a factor, because plants absorb CO_2. Carbon dioxide is responsible for a larger share of human-induced global warming than any other gas.

The atmospheric concentration of methane has also increased since 1750—by 151 percent, a level that has not been that high in the past half million years. Methane gas is linked to the use of fossil fuels, to cattle, to rice agriculture, and to landfills.

Name _____   Class _____   Date _____

Chapter 3, Geography for Life Activities, continued

The atmospheric concentration of nitrous oxide (N_2O) has increased 17 percent since 1750; it has not been this high in at least the past 1,000 years. The human contribution to atmospheric N_2O comes from agricultural soils, cattle feed lots, and the chemical industry.

CFCs are manufactured for use in plastic foams and as refrigerants, propellants, and solvents. Atmospheric concentrations of CFCs rose quickly for several decades, but more recently they have increased more slowly or have declined. This latter effect is the result of international efforts to curb CFC emissions, as they are known to destroy ozone. Replacement compounds and some other synthetic compounds are increasing in the atmosphere, and they also are greenhouse gases.

Various computer models have been developed to predict the future of global climate change. There is considerable agreement among the models, despite the high degree of complexity involved in the global climate system and uncertainties about the behavior of some phenomena. The global average surface temperature is projected to increase by 1.4 to 5.8°C between 1990 and 2100. This rate of warming is much larger than that of the 1900s and is very likely to exceed any other warming that has occurred in the last 10,000 years.

What Does Global Warming Mean for Life on Earth?

What will be the effects of this warming on the environment and people? The environmental impacts will be complex, interacting with one another and with other sources of stress, such as deforestation or pollution. The impacts will be geographically variable; at times different parts of the world may experience opposite effects. In general, the smaller the region that scientists focus on, the lower the level of certainty attached to any predictions made about the region.

In the face of climate change, some individual species will successfully adapt or move, while others will become extinct. Existing Earth ecosystems will shift their locations; new ecosystems may emerge. Rising sea levels will threaten coastal ecosystems such as mangrove forests, coral reefs, and sea grasses—some of the most diverse and productive ecosystems on Earth. Ocean ecosystems may also be affected. The faster and greater the warming, the more severe the effects will be on natural systems.

Many human systems are sensitive to climate change. These systems include water resources, agriculture and forestry, fisheries, settlements, energy, industry, insurance and other financial services, and human health. Scientists expect a variety of impacts on the hydrologic system, including changes in both the quantity and quality of streamflow and groundwater recharge. The predicted changes include less water for already water-stressed countries in central Asia, southern Africa, and around the Mediterranean Sea. The impacts of global warming on crop yields are predicted to be highly variable. Some regions will suffer and others will benefit. Farmers in many places will have to adapt to new climatic conditions.

Human settlements are vulnerable to climate change in several ways. The economic sectors (for example, agriculture or tourism) that support a city may be harmed by global warming. The physical infrastructure of a city can be damaged by flooding and landslides, which are predicted to increase in association with increased rainfall intensity and rising sea levels. The population of a city may be affected by extreme weather events (such as heat waves and violent storms), the frequency of which is expected to climb. The population can also be affected by diseases, some of which (malaria and dengue fever) are expected to extend their ranges.

The vulnerability of populations to these and other predicted impacts of global warming varies tremendously. Some places are naturally more prone to damage than others. Low-lying places are vulnerable to floods and dry places are vulnerable to droughts. In addition to such natural factors, the level of development attained by a place is of enormous significance in assessing its capacity to deal with climate change. Richer places will have an easier time, poorer places a tougher one.

The world community has attempted to reach agreement on actions to be taken in response to global warming. In 1992 the United Nations Framework Convention on Climate Change was signed by 154 states at Rio de Janeiro, and it went into force in March 1994. In 1997 the Kyoto Protocol committed the developed countries to reduce their collective greenhouse gas emissions by 5 percent from 1990 levels by 2008–2012. Since then, however, the United States, by far the world's largest producer of such emissions, has stated that it believes the protocol is unworkable. One problem that the United States has with the agreement is that it does not require developing countries, such as China or India, to reduce their emissions. The U.S. government also believes that the target reductions are unrealistic. However, even without international agreements, there are things that ordinary people can do to help the situation. Among these are planting trees and conserving energy.

You Are the Geographer

Pick a country for which you would like to be global climate change ambassador. Find out as much as you can about anticipated global climate change impacts on your particular country and what it is doing about them, including its position on the Kyoto Protocol. Then prepare a five-minute speech summarizing your information. After all ambassadors have given their speeches, have a discussion examining points of agreement and disagreement.

There are some excellent Internet sites to help you with your search. The United Nations Framework Convention on Climate Change (www.unfccc.de) includes "Country Information," which provides links to many national climate change sites, and an informative "Climate Change Information Kit." Manchester Metropolitan University's Global Climate Change Student Guide (www.docm.mmu.ac.uk/aric/gccsg/) and the U.S. Environmental Protection Agency Global Warming Site (www.epa.gov/globalwarming/) have excellent information. The site of the Intergovernmental Panel on Climate Change (a joint effort of the World Meteorological Society and the United Nations Environment Programme) summarizes the best scientific thinking on global climate change (www.ipcc.ch/). It is also possible to find sites on the web produced by global warming skeptics, but remember: most scientists who do research in this field are not skeptical about global warming or human contributions to it.

Name _____ Class _____ Date _____

Energy, or the ability to do work, is our most basic resource, because without it, no other resource could be tapped. The harnessing of vast quantities of nonrenewable energy was an important part of the Industrial Revolution. That energy fueled the amazing growth of the human population and high levels of material consumption achieved in some parts of the world. Today, measures of national income per capita and energy consumption per capita are highly correlated. This exercise focuses on factors that help explain patterns of coal production and trade.

Clearly, production of energy resources is tied to their location. Some places are endowed with oil and natural gas, others with coal or uranium, while still others have exceptional sites for the generation of electricity from water or wind. The location of such resources relative to markets is a primary determinant of whether they are tapped. Major markets for coal are electric power stations and the steel industry. Resources near these markets will be exploited ahead of those far away, other things being equal.

The size of a resource is important, too. A distant resource may be worth exploiting because it is very large and the costs of doing so can be spread over many units of production. Thus Alaska oil is tapped, despite its isolation and the severity of the environment.

Evaluating and Extracting Coal

The quality of some energy resources is highly variable. This is true of coal. Coal is ranked according to how much weight is lost when it is heated to about 950°C (1,750°F). Coals that lose the least weight and are the hardest are called anthracites. Coals that lose the most weight and are the softest are called lignite or brown coals. In between are the bituminous coals. Harder coals have higher elemental carbon contents and higher heat values. Because of its relatively low heat value, lignite is not worth transporting long distances and generally is not traded internationally.

Coal is graded as well as ranked. The grade of a coal is determined by the proportion of waste products present. These include ash and sulfur. The amount of sulfur in coal is an important consideration, because the sulfur released into the atmosphere from burning coal is the major source of acid rain. Because of this environmental issue, low-sulfur coal far from market may be mined rather than high-sulfur coal close by. This practice has occurred in the United States, where low-sulfur western coal is hauled to eastern power plants, by-passing high-sulfur eastern coal fields.

It is less costly to extract energy resources from some sites than others. Part of the reason for this is geological. The thickness, depth, and continuity of a coal seam, and its inclination to the surface vary greatly from deposit to deposit. The cost of extraction varies with these characteristics.

Technological innovations in extraction techniques have changed how resources are assessed. A coal deposit that was not worth exploiting using traditional methods of underground mining may become a money maker as a highly mechanized open pit (strip) mine. Places with the ability to acquire the newest, best technology will have an advantage over areas that may have a superior resource but inadequate capital resources. Many developing counties have exploitable energy resources, but no financing is available to develop them.

Factors Affecting Coal Production

The facilities and costs of energy transport shape the patterns of production. As transportation costs fall, resources that are more distant from markets can be tapped. Energy users are also able to locate at sites away from the places where the energy is produced. International trade in energy is encouraged. In the case of coal, giant ocean-going carriers make hauling coal halfway around the world profitable.

The quality and quantity of labor necessary to extract energy can influence patterns of production. Coal mines can shut down due to shortages of skilled labor. Corporations may choose to close mines if they cannot reach agreements with labor unions.

Political concerns often enter into decisions about energy production. At various times and places, governments have protected or subsidized their domestic energy producers against foreign competition. These policies reflect the political power of energy producers, but they are also tied to security considerations. Many national governments are concerned about becoming energy dependent on outsiders.

Environmental concerns have come to play an important role in locational decisions about energy production. All forms of energy production have negative impacts on the environment, whether on scenic views, water, air, land, flora, or fauna. Today, the costs of complying with environmental regulations must be taken into account when energy investment decisions are made. Since environmental rules differ from place to place, their impact varies geographically.

Finally, there is the weight of history. Energy production requires large outlays of money. Building a coal plant is an expensive proposition. Even if the location of the plant is no longer optimal, the expense involved in moving it is often very high. This reality, along with the spatial concentration of resources, serves as a locational brake.

A last aspect of the geography of coal worth noting is the kinds of places that have been created by coal mining. Social structure, ethnicity, religion, language, gender roles, health, dress, and other aspects of daily life in coal-mining communities were shaped by the dominant economic activity. These aspects of place are captured in music, writing, and film about coal-mining regions such as Appalachia and southern Wales.

You Are the Geographer

Use the world outline map of major coal basins and the data in Table 1 at the end of this activity to produce a map of (a) major coal producers and (b) major coal exporters linked to their destinations. Use a rectangular proportional area symbol to show production. Let a square one-tenth of an inch stand for each 10 million metric tons of production. Thus, for example, Germany will be represented by 5 such squares and South Africa

Chapter 4, Geography for Life Activities, continued

by 22. Use a colored pencil to fill in the number of squares on each country's symbol that stands for the amount of coal exported. Use proportional arrows to show the flows from the exporting nations to the destination regions. Let an arrow width of 1 inch stand for a flow of 100 million metric tons; 0.1 inch for 10 million metric tons; and a pencil line width for 1 million metric tons. Give your map a title and legend.

Use your map as the basis for writing a paragraph describing and interpreting the world pattern of coal exports. Also explain why only about 13 percent of world coal production is traded internationally, while over half of world petroleum production is. As an extension of this exercise, you may want to obtain and analyze data (from www.eia.doe.gov) on patterns of coal production within the United States.

Table 1. Major Hard Coal Producers and Exporters by Destination, 1997

Producer	Total Production	Total Exports	North America	Latin America	Europe	J, K, T, and HK	India	Southwest Asia and North Africa
Canada	41.3	36.5	0.6	2.6	6.5	25.5	—	0.7
United States	910.4	76.0	13.9	8.4	35.5	12.4	—	3.6
Colombia	30.7	26.5	3.1	0.9	19.7	—	—	1.8
Czech Rep.	16.6	6.6	—	—	6.6	—	—	—
Poland	137.8	29.5	—	—	28.7	—	—	0.5
Former USSR	305.5	20.1	0.1	—	9.6	5.6	—	4.6
China	1,372.8	30.7	—	—	1.8	27.3	0.4	—
Indonesia	55.1	41.5	1.3	1.2	6.4	23.9	1.6	0.8
South Africa	220.1	64.2	—	—	33.9	16.0	2.0	7.9
Australia	206.8	146.4	3.4	2.5	20.0	112.5	10.0	3.1
Germany*	51.2							
Spain*	13.8							
United Kingdom*	48.5							
India*	297.2							
North Korea*	24.1							
Total of Above	3731.9	478.0	25.5	15.6	168.7	220.1	14.0	23.0
World Total	3796.4	497.1						

NOTE. Data are expressed as million metric tons. Those producers marked with an * are major producers of coal but are not major exporters. North America includes Canada and the United States; Latin America includes Mexico; J, K, T, & HK = Japan, South Korea, Taiwan, and Hong Kong. The total of columns 4–9 does not exactly equal 478.0 because small amounts of exported coal went to places not listed.
Source: International Energy Agency. 1999. *Coal Information 1998.* Paris: OECD.

Name _____ Class _____ Date _____

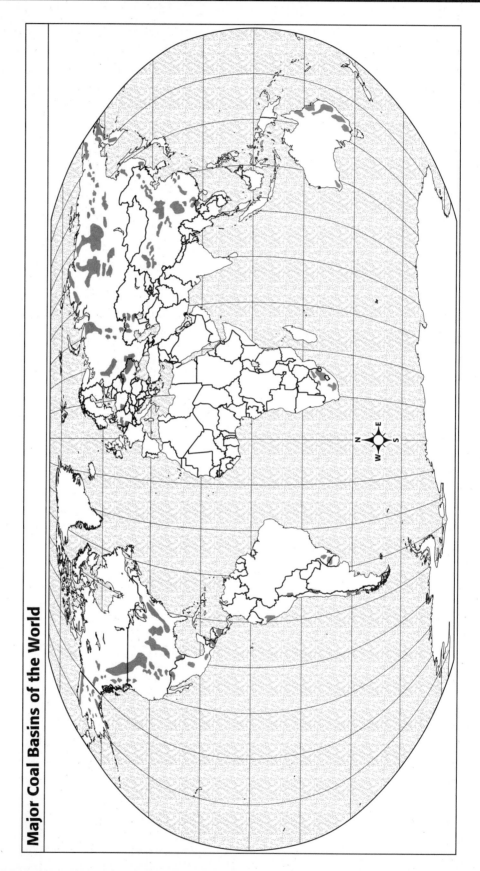

Major Coal Basins of the World

ACTIVITY **5**   Geography for Life Activities

National Geography Standard 4   **Skyscrapers and Skylines**

> *Places, and their similarities and differences, are a central concern of geography. Geographers want to know, for instance, how Philadelphia resembles Phoenix, how they differ, and why. One important characteristic of places is their buildings. Buildings are dominant elements in our visual images of places. They provide clues to the lives and jobs of the people who inhabit and use them. Thus, we "read" from a landscape of high-rise office buildings a different type of work and social setting than from an industrial park filled with warehouses and factories. We also read buildings as symbols.*

Skyscrapers are tall buildings that have usable space. They are an American invention. They evolved in the downtown setting that geographers call the Central Business District (CBD). The CBD is where the city's first-class (up-to-date and expensive) office space is concentrated. In addition to business and government offices, the CBD has hotels, entertainment facilities, and some retailing. The CBD is subdivided into core and frame. The CBD core is where the rents are highest, where the buildings are newest (and often tallest), and where human interactions are at the highest organizational levels. As geographer Larry Ford says in his book, *Cities and Buildings: Skyscrapers, Skid Rows, and Suburbs,* "it is the place where movers and shakers meet to move and shake." The CBD frame supports the core and contains parking lots, office suppliers, janitorial services, and eating, drinking, and sleeping establishments. The boundary between the core and frame shifts, as the core expands in one direction and contracts in another.

The History of the Business District

The world's first specialized business district probably emerged in London, where it was well established by 1700. London's role in world trade gave rise to banking and insurance activities. These activities benefited from clustering, creating a quarter where other land uses, such as residential and industrial, became scarcer, in part because they could not afford the rents. At this stage, the buildings that offices occupied were little different in appearance from those of any other activity.

As businesses became larger during the Victorian era, some gained enough wealth to build taller. While in earlier eras only churches and town halls had soaring towers, now others could compete for height. Several technological developments facilitated tall buildings. These developments included the passenger elevator (1856), the electric light (1879) run from a central station power (1882), and steel-frame construction (1883). Transport innovations, including the horsecar (a horse-drawn wagon on tracks), commuter rail lines, cable cars, electric streetcars, and subways and elevated railways, made it possible for ever larger numbers of people to converge on a densely built-up CBD from distant residential districts.

Through the end of the 1800s, most office buildings contained a mix of small tenants. Large corporations came along in the early years of the 1900s. These corporations needed lots of space under one roof (for convenience) and wanted it in a tall building for prestige. Moreover, people with only information to carry can travel easily by elevator, in contrast to people handling goods, who work more efficiently in horizontal spaces. The high-density CBD created by skyscrapers maximized opportunities for interaction, an important element in business decision-making and innovation.

The Skyscraper Dominates

The skyscraper and skyline as symbols of the American city took hold in the 1920s. Numerous cities that up to that time did not have a building over 20 stories in height acquired one or more. These skyscrapers tended to attract activity and investment to them, thereby draining it from other parts of the CBD. The areas left behind became marginal and joined the frame. In this way, skyscrapers were forces of differentiation in the American city.

In the 1920s, skyscraper design began to celebrate height rather than ignore it. In the 1920s New York City acquired dozens of buildings over 500 feet tall and two over 1,000 feet—the Chrysler Building and the Empire State Building. The latter remained the tallest building in the world until Chicago's Sears Tower surpassed it in the mid-1970s.

The Great Depression of the 1930s brought financial ruin to many skyscraper owners and builders. Skyscraper construction ceased in many places, not to resume until the mid-1960s. Because of the glut of space and the low rents, firms and organizations normally priced out of skyscrapers moved in. This meant, however, lots of empty space in marginal buildings, which contributed to the emergence of skid rows on CBD edges.

Some new civic projects went forth during the Depression, taking advantage of lowered property costs. For example, the spectacular Rockefeller Center was built in New York City in the 1930s. It included innovations that would come to typify skyscrapers built much later: underground parking, subterranean walkways, air conditioning, and pedestrian plazas.

Several trends affected CBDs from the 1950s. Some corporate offices suburbanized, especially those that performed routine functions or needed lots of computer space. They did not need a central location or a skyscraper, and instead sought out a campus-style settings in the suburbs. Massive urban renewal projects, heavily subsidized by the federal government, cleared large areas of downtown Pittsburgh, Baltimore, Cleveland, St. Louis, and other cities. Some cleared areas became home to gleaming new towers, built in a minimalist Modern style.

After World War II, the big story of the American economy has been its shift away from the production of goods and toward the production of information, whose handlers are partial to skyscrapers. The globalization of the world economy has created new demand for prestige office space not only from American firms, but from the growing number of foreign firms operating in the United States. Today, there are over 900 buildings in the United States that reach or exceed 400 feet (about 30 stories) in height. These appear in about 70 different metropolitan areas.

You Are the Geographer

Work in small groups to answer the questions. Consult maps as necessary. For example, if you do not know which cities are associated with the oil industry, look at a map of U.S.

oil fields. After you are done, have a class discussion about what you learned. Larry Ford devised a measure that he named the "Skyline Score" that allows the comparison of city skylines while taking into account metropolitan population. It incorporates the number of tall buildings (here we use buildings 400 feet or taller) and the heights of the three tallest. So a city increases its score both by having many tall buildings and by having several extremely tall ones.

Calculate the scores for each metropolitan area using the table at the end of this activity. The formula for the skyline score, S, is equal to $(B/P \times H)$, where B is the number of buildings over 400 feet tall, P is the metropolitan statistical area (MSA) population in millions, and H is the combined height of the three tallest buildings in thousands of feet. Thus, for New York, $S = (291/20.1) \times 3.248 = 47.0$. To obtain H for cities with fewer than three buildings =400 feet, use the bracketed numbers, which are the heights of the next tallest buildings. It is worth noting that when the World Trade Center was standing, its two towers (1368 and 1362 feet) brought New York's score to 57.4, higher than Chicago's.

1. In general, what is the relationship between metropolitan area size and the number of skyscrapers? How do you explain it?

2. What is happening in New York and Chicago (beyond sheer numbers of people) to generate such tall skyscrapers and such concentrations of skyscrapers? Why is Los Angeles so different?

3. Look at maps of the locations of the CBDs of Boston, San Francisco, and Pittsburgh. Is there anything about their sites that might encourage going vertical?

4. What might be the effect of being near a large metropolitan area? Can you see any examples of this "shadow" effect?

5. What are some examples of the opposite situation—regional capitals with large hinterlands containing few competing cities?

6. Skyscrapers are major opportunities for investment. (a) What are some cities that specialize in the financial sector (banking and insurance), and therefore could be expected to have funds to invest in skyscrapers? (b) What are some cities that have had lots of money to invest all at once (during boom periods) because they specialize in the energy sector?

7. Which city traditionally specialized in steel (think of coal and iron ore) and glass production and might use skyscrapers to showcase these technologies? What other cities specialized in heavy industry, but have not had the same success in switching to the kinds of white collar jobs that get housed in skyscrapers?

8. Some cities have placed significant limits on building heights. Examples include Washington, D.C. (where there are no 400-foot buildings; all those listed in the table are in Baltimore); in the past, Philadelphia; and recently, San Francisco. What might these places be protecting?

9. Cities sometimes compete with one another for symbols of city achievement and

Name _____ Class _____ Date _____

pride. What are some likely pairs of competitors in such "skyscraper sweepstakes"?

10. What do you think will be the effect of the events of September 11, 2001 on attitudes toward skyscrapers and on their rate of construction?

Table 1. Skyscrapers in the 35 Largest U. S. Metropolitan Areas

Metropolitan Area	Number of Skyscrapers (≥400 feet)	Heights of Three Tallest Buildings (feet)	Metropolitan Area Population (1998) (millions)	Skyline Score
1. New York	291	1250, 1046, 952	20.1	_____
2. Los Angeles	32	1018, 858, 750	15.8	_____
3. Chicago	128	1450, 1136, 1127	8.8	_____
4. Washington-Baltimore	6	529, 509, 493	7.3	_____
5. San Francisco	40	853, 779, 695	6.8	_____
6. Philadelphia	24	945, 848, 792	6.0	_____
8. Detroit	16	725, 619, 557	5.5	_____
9. Dallas-Ft. Worth	35	921, 886, 787	4.8	_____
10. Houston	42	1002, 972, 901	4.4	_____
11. Atlanta	24	1023, 871, 820	3.7	_____
12. Miami-Ft. Lauderdale	23	789, 764, 625	3.7	_____
13. Seattle	19	954, 740, 730	3.	_____
14. Phoenix	2	486, 407, [393]	2.9	_____
15. Cleveland	10	950, 708, 658	2.9	_____
16. Minneapolis-St. Paul	21	775, 774, 773	2.8	_____
17. San Diego	5	500, 499, 497	2.8	_____
18. St. Louis	5	593, 588, 557	2.6	_____
19. Denver	14	714, 709, 698	2.4	_____
20. Pittsburgh	16	841, 725, 635	2.3	_____
21. Tampa-St. Petersburg	7	579, 577, 537	2.3	_____
22. Portland, Oregon	4	546, 536, 509	2.1	_____
23. Cincinnati	7	574, 495, 468	1.9	_____
24. Kansas City	10	632, 590, 504	1.7	_____
25. Sacramento	1	423, [370], [367]	1.7	_____
26. Milwaukee	4	625, 549, 426	1.6	_____
27. Norfolk-Virginia Beach	0	[354], [302], [283]	1.5	_____
28. Indianapolis	5	820, 533, 504	1.5	_____
30. Orlando	3	441, 416, 409	1.5	_____
31. Columbus	10	624, 555, 530	1.5	_____
32. Charlotte	9	871, 658, 588	1.4	_____
33. Las Vegas	8	525, 508, 483	1.3	_____
34. New Orleans	11	697, 645, 531	1.3	_____
35. Salt Lake City	2	422, 420, [348]	1.3	_____

Note. The skyline score has been modified from Larry Ford's 1994 book, *Cities and Buildings,* p. 51.

Name _____ Class _____ Date _____

Where Are Cars Made?

Geography for Life Activities

Economic geography is concerned with the distribution of economic activity.
Economic activity includes production, trade, and consumption. Key questions
for economic geographers include, "Why are _____ [fill in the blank with any
commodity—from apples to zithers] produced here and not there?" "What
products are exchanged among various places and why?" "Why have some parts
of the world achieved high levels of consumption, while in others millions of
people barely consume enough to survive?"

This exercise focuses on where one particular commodity—automobiles—is made. It also
examines patterns of automobile trade. For the developed market economies, automobile
manufacturing was the key industry of the middle decades of the 1900s and the most
important engine of growth until the middle 1970s. Many poorer countries viewed it as
key to national economic development. The scale of the automobile industry and its linkages with many other industries give it great economic weight. Automobile manufacturing
employs 3 to 4 million people worldwide. Another 9 to 10 million work in factories making materials and components. When the people who sell and service cars are added, a
total of about 20 million people is reached.

Car manufacturing is dominated by a limited number of giant corporations. The
world's top 10 car makers produce 71 percent of the world's cars. The top 20 produce
almost 90 percent of the total. All these firms manufacture, or at the very least, assemble,
cars in more than one country. This practice makes them transnational firms. Typically,
their cars are put together from materials and components manufactured in many different countries. Car manufacturers and their products provide good evidence of what we
call the global economy.

Understanding the Industry

Automobile manufacturing is somewhat market-oriented. This means that car production is attracted to where car customers are located. An automobile plant is a major
investment and is only feasible if it produces many cars. Thus, car plants tend to be large
and relatively few. The plants tend to be located within large, wealthy consumer markets
(Western Europe, North America, and Japan). There are a couple of reasons for this.
First, it was within such markets (in Europe and the United States) that car manufacturing began. The great expense of building car plants means that their locations do not
change very rapidly. Second, it costs more to transport cars than to transport the materials and components that go into them. So it makes sense to gather the inputs together
near where you are going to sell the cars and assemble them there. Third, making cars
requires skilled labor, abundant in the world's developed or semi-developed economies.

So the pattern of car manufacturing is different from that of activities drawn toward
cheap labor (such as shoe production) or toward raw materials (such as processing milk
into cheese). The cost of labor is still also a factor. For example, cheaper labor costs in
southern Europe than in northern Europe helped draw car plants to Spain. Likewise,

Mexico's low labor costs have attracted car plants there. In both these cases, however, expanding markets that could be efficiently served from these places were also important considerations.

Factors Influencing the Industry

The locational decisions of automobile companies are greatly affected by the policies of national governments. In order to protect their own (domestic) automobile manufacturers, many countries have limited the number of foreign-made cars allowed in. Before World War II, many countries had high tariffs (taxes) on imported cars. These tariffs were designed to discourage imports and encourage foreign branch plants and/or domestic producers. Today, tariffs on cars are generally low in the major developed county markets. However, non-tariff barriers are still common; these barriers include quotas, such as those negotiated between Japan and the United States and Japan and the European Union, restricting Japanese imports.

Such barriers as tariffs and quotas serve to encourage automobile makers to build overseas production plants in their major markets. Ford and General Motors produce a higher share of their cars abroad than do any other firms in the world. Since the 1980s, Japanese auto makers have built production plants in both North America and Europe. Japanese car plants produced nearly 1.6 million cars in the United States in 1999, nearly 28 percent of the total. Honda, Toyota, Nissan, Mitsubishi, Subaru, and Mazda all have American plants. In Europe, Japanese car plants are found in Great Britain and the Netherlands.

National governments have increased pressure on foreign firms to build overseas production plants on their soil by requiring specific levels of local content in cars built by foreign producers. In other words, national governments have required a certain share (by value) of the components and materials in cars made by foreign firms to be domestically produced. This policy prevents foreign firms from making all the parts of their vehicles at home and doing just the final assembly in the country where the car is to be sold. The required level of local content is usually between 50 and 90 percent, often rising over a period of several years.

Local content requirements have long been a feature of developing country policies toward foreign auto makers. They help spread the wealth and technological development generated by auto production through the national economy of the developing country. The goal is the eventual creation of a domestic auto industry. National governments have also required foreign firms producing in their countries to export some of the vehicles made there, boosting the country's foreign earnings.

High tariffs, import restrictions, and local content requirements, together with financial incentives and tax breaks, have helped bring foreign branch plants to Argentina, Brazil, and Mexico. South Korea, on the other hand, discouraged both imported cars and foreign branch plants. Instead, Korea has built its own domestic automobile industry (which is not to say that this was accomplished without foreign expertise and investment). Currently, Malaysia's government-owned car maker, Proton, is marketing its first home-designed and home-built car.

You Are the Geographer

Task 1. Use the data in Table 1 to write a two to three paragraph summarizing the global pattern of automobile production in 1995 and how it differs from the 1960 pattern.

Task 2. Use the information in Tables 2 and 3 to write a two to three paragraphs summarizing world patterns of automobile trade.

Task 3. Pick a developing country and adopt the point of view of its Minister of Economic Development. Select an automaker and draft a letter advocating your country as a good location for that firm to build a plant. Use reference books or the Internet to find out relevant information about your country, such as population and income (these influence the market for cars), level of education (this affects the skill level of workers), export facilities that could be used to distribute the cars to other countries, available raw materials, and so on. Are there any reasons why the particular firm you are approaching (or its home country) might want to invest in your country (for example, ethnic ties, need to strengthen political links, trade relationships)? What kinds of incentives will you offer and what kinds of rules will you impose?

Table 1. Automobile Production by Major Countries, 1960 and 1995.

Country	1960 Production (000 units)	1960 World Share (%)	1995 Production (000 units)	1995 World Share (%)
France	1,175	9.0	3,050	8.2
Germany	1,817	14.0	4,360	11.8
Italy	596	4.6	1,423	3.8
Spain	43	0.3	1,959	5.3
Sweden	108	0.8	388	1.1
United Kingdom	1,353	10.4	1,532	4.1
Canada	323	2.5	1,339	3.6
United States	6,675	51.4	6,350	17.1
Japan	165	1.3	7,611	20.6
Korea	N/A	N/A	2,003	5.4
Malaysia	N/A	N/A	195	0.5
Taiwan	N/A	N/A	282	0.8
Argentina	30	0.2	227	0.6
Brazil	38	0.3	1,303	3.5
Mexico	28	0.2	699	1.9
Australia	N/A	N/A	292	0.8
Czech Republic	N/A	N/A	228	0.6
Poland	N/A	N/A	392	1.1
Total of above	12,351	95.0	36,633	90.8
World total	12,999	100.0	37,045	100.0

N/A = Data not available.

Table 2. Leading Automobile Exporting Countries

Country	Share of the World's Exports	
	1980	1995
Germany	21.0	18.6
Japan	19.8	17.7
USA	12.7	11.5
Canada	6.9	9.6
France	9.9	7.3
Belgium-Luxembourg	4.9	5.3
Spain	1.8	4.9
UK	5.8	4.4
Italy	4.5	4.0
Mexico	0.3	3.1
Sweden	2.8	N/A
Korea	0.1	2.0
Netherlands	1.1	1.5
Austria	0.5	N/A
Brazil	1.1	0.6
TOTAL	93.2	90.5

N/A=Data not available.

Table 3. Destinations of Automobile Exports, Selected Countries, 1994.

	Share by Destination (%)					
	Europe	North America	Latin America	Africa	Asia/Oceania	Southwest Asia
Japan	27.6	47.4	6.5	1.0	11.7	5.8
USA	12.0	55.0	8.0	0.2	24.0	1.0
Canada	0.8	98.9	0.1	—	0.3	—
Germany	77.0	9.0	1.0	0.5	11.0	1.0
France	86.0	0.2	5.6	2.0	3.0	1.0
Italy	91.0	0.2	2.8	1.0	5.0	0.2
Spain	93.1	2.0			1.0	
UK	85.5	4.9	0.5	0.4	6.2	2.0
Brazil	7.3	—	92.7	—	—	—
Mexico	87.7	8.9	—	—	—	—
South Korea	22.1	36.2	14.0	2.3	18.4	7.0

Name _____ Class _____ Date _____

Geography for Life Activities

Landform Postcards from National Parks

This exercise is about landforms in the national parks of the United States and Canada. This exercise will help you learn about landforms, and it is also designed to encourage you to go see them "up close and personal" in our national parks. To complete the exercise you will need to access the websites of the U.S. National Park Service (www.nps.gov) and/or Parks Canada (www.parkscanada.gc.ca) or published guides to the national parks. A widely available and useful one is National Geographic's Guide to the National Parks of the United States.

Various types of landforms are listed below with brief descriptions. You are to write and illustrate a series of "postcards" from parks where these features are found. For example, if you decided you wanted to produce a postcard on hot springs, first you would use one of the websites or a book to find a national park where they are found. After searching for information, you might find some details and illustrations of hot springs in Lassen Volcanic National Park in California or Kootenay National Park in British Columbia. On one side of your postcard, you will draw a sketch or diagram of hot springs at the park and on the other you will write a paragraph describing them and explaining the process that formed them. Other interesting details, such as associated flora and fauna, can be mentioned. If you have a chance, make postcards on several different landforms from several different parks.

Below is a selection of landforms with basic definitions. One good place to look for additional terms or for more detailed explanations of terms is on the National Park Service website, which includes discussions of landforms and a glossary from the United States Geological Survey (USGS). Various dictionaries of physical geography terms also are available.

VOLCANIC LANDFORMS

Shield volcano. A volcano built of layers of fluid basaltic lava that is released in quiet eruptions with few explosions. The lava forms a gently sloping dome that resembles an inverted saucer.

Composite volcano. A volcano built of alternating layers of lava and tephra (also called pyroclastic material), such as ash and cinders. A conical mountain is the result.

Lava dome. A volcano built of thick, pasty lava that cannot flow far. The lava bulges up from the vent and the dome grows mostly by expansion from below.

Cinder cone. A volcano built of tephra. The steepness of its slopes depends upon the size of particles being ejected, with smaller particles supporting steeper slopes. Cinder cones are usually small, no more than 1,500 feet high.

Caldera. A huge, basin-shaped steep-sided depression with a diameter many times larger than that of the original vent. A caldera can result when a volcano explodes or collapses.

Volcanic neck. A mass of solidified lava filling the central volcanic vent. It can be left isolated and resemble a small, sharp spire as material around it is eroded.

DIASTROPHIC LANDFORMS (landforms that result from the disturbance and dislocation of Earth's crust)

Folded mountains. Mountains that have been bent into a massive fold or ridge by Earth movements. The arch or crest of a fold in rock strata is an *anticline*. The trough or inverted arch is a *syncline*.

Fault. A fault is a break in Earth's crust along which movement has taken place. The movement can be horizontal, vertical, or both.

Fault scarp. A fault scarp is a cliff formed by faulting. The lower side of the fault has experienced relative downward movement.

Fault-block mountains. These mountains are created when a surface block is faulted and uplifted on one side but not the other. The block is tilted asymmetrically, with a steep slope along the fault scarp and a gentle slope on the opposite side.

Horst and graben. A horst is an uplifted block of crust between two parallel faults; a graben is a dropped-down block between two parallel faults.

FLUVIAL LANDFORMS (landforms created by running water)

Gorge. A narrow, deep valley with steep sides. A **canyon** is a large gorge.

Floodplain. A flattish valley floor formed by deposits of sediment (alluvium) carried down by a river. When the river overflows its banks, a layer of sediment is deposited, so that the level of the floodplain rises over time. Usually the floodplain is highest nearest the river at its **natural levees.**

Bluff. A steep slope at the outer edge of a floodplain, often formed by the river cutting into the valley sides.

Delta. A sometimes fan-shaped deposit of alluvium built up at the mouth of a river when it dumps more material there than can removed by tides and currents. Deposition occurs because the stream slows down as it meets the sea, and as speed is reduced, so is the stream's ability to transport its load.

Stream terrace. A fall in sea level or an uplift of land will cause a stream to cut down into its floodplain, eventually creating a new floodplain at a lower level. On either side of the stream, the old floodplain, above the level of the new one, becomes a stream terrace. This process may happen many times, resulting in a series of terraces.

Entrenched meander. A meander is a wide loop in a river that swings from side to side as it flows across a flat floodplain. A fall in sea level or an uplift in land can cause such a river to cut downward, incising itself in narrow gorges and creating entrenched meanders.

FEATURES CREATED BY UNDERGROUND WATER

Karst. A limestone region with underground drainage and landforms created when water containing carbon dioxide calcium carbonate in the limestone dissolves. **Caves, sinkholes,** and **dolines** (closed hollows near the surface) are common.

Hot spring. Beneath Earth's surface, water comes in contact with hot rocks or magma. Pressure forces the heated water through cracks to the surface where it emerges as a hot spring. Hot springs water that is rich in lime often creates deposits of a porous calcium carbonate rock called tufa.

LANDFORMS OF ARID LANDS

Arroyo, wash, coulee. The normally dry bed of an ephemeral desert stream, usually flat-bottomed and steep-sided.

Playa. A dry lake bed in an area of interior drainage. A playa can become a **playa lake** when water flows into it as a result of rainfall or flood. Evaporation often leaves behind salts.

Mesa. A flat, table-like upland with steep slopes on all sides. A hard top layer has resisted erosion and and protected weaker layers beneath. A small mesa is called a **butte**.

Sand dune. A mound or low hill of loose, windblown sand that is deposited when the wind transporting sand is slowed down. The **barchan** usually occurs as an individual dune. It is crescent-shaped with the horns of the dune pointing downwind. Sand is deposited over the top and around the edges. **Transverse dunes** are less uniformly crescent-shaped and occur where there is a larger sand supply than in barchan locations. Transverse dunes line up in parallel waves across the land. Both kinds of dunes migrate downwind.

Alluvial fan. A deposit of sediment laid down by a swift-running mountain stream as it flows out onto a plain and slows down. When one part of the fan is built up, the stream migrates to another section and builds it up. Eventually the whole fan is covered with sediment.

Badlands. Unconsolidated material in arid lands that has been intricately gullied and formed into a fantastic maze of ridges and ledges. Because of rapid erosion, plants have trouble getting established, so badlands typically are barren as well as impassable.

GLACIAL LANDFORMS (erosional and depositional)

Cirque. A deep rounded hollow with steep sides at the head of a glacial trough (valley). A cirque is the first landform produced by an alpine glacier. Fragments of rock are quarried by the ice. If the glacial ice in a cirque has melted away and the cirque is filled with water, it is called a **tarn**. An **arête** is a sharp mountain ridge created by the erosion of two adjacent cirques. A **horn** is a pyramidal peak formed by the erosion of three or more adjacent cirques. The Matter*horn* is a famous example.

U-shaped valley. A valley that forms a "U" in cross-section (rather than a "V"). The gouging action of a glacier as it moves down a former river valley sculpts this shape. Sometimes the valley is also straightened.

Hanging valley. A tributary valley that enters a main valley from quite a height above it, so that a stream flowing from the tributary valley enters the main valley as a waterfall. The main valley was more quickly eroded by its glacier than the tributary valley.

Till plain. An irregular but relatively flat surface of low rises and shallow depressions created by the uneven deposition of **glacial till** (rock debris laid down by moving ice).

Moraine. An irregular deposit of material that has been transported by a glacier. Deposition along the side of a glacier creates a **lateral moraine,** while deposition at the outermost extent of ice advance creates a **terminal moraine.**

Drumlin. An elongated hill of unsorted till like a moraine but much smaller. Drumlins are shaped like eggs sliced in half the long way. They are probably the result of ice re-advancing onto an area where till was previously deposited. Drumlins occur in swarms.

Outwash plain. Smooth, flattish alluvial plain formed by streams of meltwater from a glacier. These streams carry away material from moraines and spread it over large areas.

COASTAL LANDFORMS

Beach. A strip of land bordering the sea, usually lying between high and low water marks, and having an accumulation of sediment. This sediment is exposed to the sculpting forces of tides, waves, currents, stream outflow, changes in oceanic water level, and in some places, ice.

Estuary. The mouth of a river where fresh and salt water mix and where tides ebb and flow. Many estuaries are river valleys that have been flooded by the sea due to rising sea levels and/or subsiding (sinking) coastal lowlands.

Barrier island. A long narrow sand bar, often paralleling the coast, built up in shallow off-shore waters. Barrier islands are probably the result of deposition where large waves begin to break in the shallow waters of continental shelves.

Lagoon. A shallow stretch of water between a barrier island (or a **barrier reef,** a type of coral reef) and the mainland. Over time, deposition (by coastal streams, wind, and tides) in lagoons often turns them into **mudflats** and eventually meadows.

Spit. A linear deposit of sediment attached to land at one end and extending into open water at the other. Spits are built by longshore currents, in which water moves roughly parallel to the shoreline and generally downwind. At the mouth of a bay the current drifts into deeper water, its flow speed is slowed, and its sediment is deposited.

Fjord. A steep-sided glacial trough partly drowned by the sea. Sometimes fjords extend 100 miles inland from the coast.

ACTIVITY (8) — Geography for Life Activities

National Geography Standard 17

Mark Twain's
Life on the Mississippi

Mark Twain was the pseudonym of Samuel Langhorne Clemens (1835–1910). Many of his fiction and nonfiction writings provide lively descriptions of American places in the last third of the 1800s. Several of his books, including his most famous novel, The Adventures of Huckleberry Finn, *are set along the Mississippi River. Mark Twain spent much of his boyhood in Hannibal, Missouri, a Mississippi River port. As a young man, he worked as a steamboat pilot on the Mississippi.* Life on the Mississippi *illustrates many ways in which the river and life on it had changed between 1860 and 1882.*

Often works of literature paint vivid portraits of places. In this exercise you will read excerpts from Mark Twain's 1883 book *Life on the Mississippi*. After you are done reading, write an essay explaining how the passages illustrate three essential elements of geography: *places and regions, human systems,* and *environment and society.* Be sure to address how the physical and human geography of the Mississippi River Valley was changing through time.

From Chapter III, "Frescoes From the Past"

The river's earliest commerce was in great barges—keelboats, broadhorns. They floated and sailed from the upper rivers to New Orleans, changed cargoes there, and were tediously warped and poled back by hand. A voyage down and back sometimes occupied nine months. In time this commerce increased until it gave employment to hordes of rough and hardy men. . . .

By and by the steamboat intruded. Then, for fifteen or twenty years, these men continued to run their keelboats down-stream, and the steamers did all of the up-stream business, the keelboatmen selling their boats in New Orleans, and returning home as deck passengers in the steamers.

But after a while the steamboats so increased in number and in speed that they were able to absorb the entire commerce; and then keelboating died a permanent death. The keelboatman became a deck hand, or a mate, or a pilot on the steamer; and when steamer-berths were not open to him, he took a berth on a Pittsburgh coal-flat, or on a pine-raft constructed in the forests up toward the sources of the Mississippi.

From Chapter XI, "The River Rises"

As I have said, the big rise brought a new world under my vision. By the time the river was over its banks we had forsaken our old paths and were hourly over bars that had stood ten feet out of water before; we were shaving stumpy shores, like that at the foot of Madrid Bend, which I had always seen avoided before; we were clattering through chutes like that of 82, where the opening at the foot was an unbroken wall of timber till our nose was almost at the very spot. . . .

Behind other islands we found wretched little farms, and wretcheder little log-cabins; there were crazy rail fences sticking a foot or two above the water, with one or two jeans-clad, chills-wracked, yellow-faced male miserables roosting on the top-rail, elbows on knees, jaws in hands, grinding tobacco and discharging the result at floating chips through crevices left by lost teeth; while the rest of the family and the few farm animals were huddled together in an empty wood-flat riding at her moorings close at hand. In this flatboat the family would have to cook and eat and sleep for a lesser or greater number of days (or possibly weeks), until the river should fall two or three feet and let them get back to their log-cabin and their chills again—chills being a merciful provision of an all-wise Providence to enable them to take exercise without exertion. And this sort of watery camping out was a thing which these people were rather liable to be treated to a couple of times a year: by the December rise out of the Ohio, and the June rise out of the Mississippi.

From Chapter XVII, "Cut-offs and Stephen"

The water cuts the alluvial banks of the "lower" river into deep horseshoe curves; so deep, indeed, that in some places if you were to get ashore at one extremity of the horseshoe and walk across the neck, half or three quarters of a mile, you could sit down and rest a couple of hours while your steamer was coming around the long elbow, at a speed of ten miles an hour, to take you aboard again. When the river is rising fast, some scoundrel whose plantation is back in the country, and therefore of inferior value, has only to watch his chance, cut a little gutter across the narrow neck of land some dark night, and turn the water into it, and in a wonderfully short time a miracle has happened: to wit, the whole Mississippi has taken possession of that little ditch, and placed the countryman's plantation on its bank (quadrupling its value), and that other party's formerly valuable plantation finds itself away out yonder on a big island; the old watercourse around it will soon shoal up, boats cannot approach within ten miles of it, and down goes its value to a fourth of its former worth. Watches are kept on those narrow necks, at needful times, and if a man happens to be caught cutting a ditch across them, the chances are all against his ever having another opportunity to cut a ditch.

Pray observe some of the effects of this ditching business. . . . [T]he Mississippi between Cairo and New Orleans was twelve hundred and fifteen miles long one hundred and seventy-six years ago. . . . [I]ts length is only nine hundred and seventy-three miles at present.

The towboat and the railroad had done their work, and done it well and completely. The mighty bridge, stretching along over our heads, had done its share in the slaughter and spoilation.

. . . alas for the wood-yard man! He used to fringe the river all the way; his close-ranked merchandise stretched from the one city [St. Louis] to the other [New Orleans], along the banks, and he sold uncountable cords of it every year for cash on the nail; but all the scattering boats that are left burn coal now, and the seldomest spectacle on the Mississippi to-day is a wood-pile. Where now is the once wood-yard man?

From Chapter XXIII, "Travelling Incognito"

We put ashore a well-dressed lady and gentleman, and two well-dressed, lady-like young girls. . . . No carriage was waiting. The party moved off as if they not expected any, and struck down a winding country road afoot.

But the mystery was explained when we got under way again; for these people were evidently bound for a large town which lay shut in behind a tow-head (i.e., new island) a couple of miles below this landing. . . . I suspected it might be St. Genevieve—and so it proved to be. Observe what this eccentric river had been about: it had built up this huge useless tow-head directly in front of this town, cut off its river communications, fenced it away completely, and made a "country" town of it. It is a fine old place, too, and deserved a better fate. It was settled by the French, and is a relic of a time when one could travel from the mouths of the Mississippi to Quebec and be on French territory and under French rule all the way.

From Chapter XXVIII, "Uncle Mumford Unloads"

As we approached famous and formidable Plum Point, darkness fell, but that was nothing to shudder about—in these modern times. For now the national government has turned the Mississippi into a sort of two-thou-sand-mile torch-light procession. In the head of every crossing, and in the foot of every crossing, the government has set up a clear-burning lamp. . . .

But this thing has knocked the romance out of piloting, to a large extent. It and some other things together, have knocked all the romance out of it. For instance, the peril from snags is not now what it once was. The government's snag-boats go patrolling up and down, in these matter-of-fact days, pulling the river's teeth; they have rooted out all the old clusters which made many localities so formidable; and they allow no new ones to collect. . . .

The military engineers of the [United States River] Commission have taken upon their shoulders the job of making the Mississippi over again,— a job transcended in size by only the original job of creating it. They are building wing-dams here and there, to deflect the current; and dikes to confine it in narrower bounds; and other dikes to make it stay there; and for unnumbered miles along the Mississippi, they are felling the timber-front for fifty yards back, with the purpose of shaving the bank down to low-water mark with the slant of a house roof, and ballasting it with stones; and in many places they have protected the wasting shores with rows of piles.

From Chapter XXXIV, "Tough Yarns"

A Mr. H. furnished some minor details of fact concerning this region which I would have hesitated to believe if I had not known him to be a steamboat mate. . . . Among other things, he said that Arkansas had been injured and kept back by generations of exaggerations concerning the mosquitoes there. One may smile, said he, and turn the matter off as being a small thing; but when you come to look at the effects produced, in the way of discourage-ment of immigration, and diminished values of property, it was quite the opposite of a small thing. . . .

These mosquitoes had been persistently represented as being formidable and lawless; whereas "the truth is, they are feeble, insignificant in size, diffident to a fault, sensitive"—and so on, and so on; you would have supposed he was talking about his family. But if he was soft on the Arkansas mosquitoes, he was hard enough on the mosquitoes of Lake Providence [Louisiana] to make up for it—"those Lake Providence colossi," as he finely called them. He said that two of them could whip a dog, and that four of them could hold a man down; and except help come, they would kill him—"butcher him," as he expressed it.

From Chapter XXXV, "Vicksburg During the Trouble [Civil War]"

Apparently, nearly all river towns, big and little, have made up their minds that they must look mainly to railroads for wealth and upbuilding, henceforth. They are acting up this idea. The signs are, that the next twenty years will bring about noteworthy changes in the Valley, in the direction of increased population and wealth, and in the intellectual advancement and the liberalizing of opinion which go naturally with these.

From Chapter XLIV, "City Sights"

The old French part of New Orleans—anciently the Spanish part—bears no resemblance to the American end of the city: the American end which lies beyond the intervening brick business-centre. The houses are massed in blocks; are austerely plain and dignified; uniform of pattern, with here and there a departure from it with pleasant effect; all are plastered on the outside, and nearly all have long, iron-railed verandas running along the several stories. Their chief beauty is the deep, warm varicolored stain with which time and the weather have enriched the plaster. It harmonizes with all the surroundings, and has as natural a look of belonging there as has the flush upon the sunset clouds. This charming decoration cannot be successfully imitated; neither is it to be found elsewhere in America.

From Chapter LX, "Speculations and Conclusions"

Minneapolis is situated at the falls of St. Anthony, which stretch across the river, fifteen hundred feet, and have a fall of eighty-two feet—a waterpower which, by art, has been made of inestimable value, business-wise, though somewhat to the damage of the Falls as a spectacle, or as a background against which to get your photograph taken.

Thirty flouring mills turn out two million barrels of the very choicest of flour every year; twenty sawmills produce two hundred million feet of lumber annually; then there are woollen mills, cotton mills, paper and oil mills; and sash, nail, furniture, barrel, and other factories without number, so to speak. . . .

Sixteen railroads meet in Minneapolis, and sixty-five passenger trains arrive and depart daily.

Name _____ Class _____ Date _____

 ACTIVITY **9**   Geography for Life Activities

National Geography Standard 11   **The Geography of
                                               Canadian Agriculture**

*Agriculture is an important economic activity. It alters natural environments
and shapes landscapes. It displays tremendous variation from place to place.
These characteristics make agriculture a subject of great interest to geographers.*

Raw and manufactured products from Canadian farms account for 10 percent of the
country's economy. More than half of these products are exported. Farms occupy about 7
percent of Canadian territory. Almost all of them are to be found south of the 55th parallel, and in the eastern part of the country—most are south of the 50th parallel. About 3
percent of Canada's 31 million people live on farms.

In this exercise you will learn how Canadian agriculture varies from one province to
another by working with data from the 1996 Canadian Census of Agriculture. Additional
information is available at the website for Statistics Canada (www.statcan.ca). You will
need a calculator. Write all your answers on a separate sheet of paper.

You Are the Geographer

1. Begin by labeling Canada's 13 political subdivisions (10 provinces and three territories) on an outline map of Canada. Use your textbook or an atlas to find the names.

2. Study Table 1. What three political units are missing from the table? Why is agricultural production so limited in these places that they are omitted from most tables of
agricultural data? What alternative kinds of primary (extractive) economic activity
might occur there?

3. Complete column 4 in Table 1. Apart from Prince Edward Island, which three
provinces have the highest shares of their land in farms? What can you say about
average farm size in these provinces, compared to the rest of Canada ?

4. Which two provinces in Canada generate the largest "gross farm receipts"? (Note: this
figure does not tell you about farm profits, since it does not take into account farm
expenditures, but it does tell you about how big an enterprise farming is.) Complete
column 7 of Table 1. Together, what proportion of Canada's total "gross farm
receipts" do these two represent?

5. What share of Canada's "gross farm receipts" is generated in the Atlantic provinces
(New Brunswick, Newfoundland, Nova Scotia, and Prince Edward Island)? Does this
mean that farming is unimportant locally? Why or why not?

6. In North America, dairying is found in two general types of locations. First, cool,
moist regions that have trouble competing with warmer climate zones in the production of many crops often turn to dairying. Second, dairying areas develop near
metropolitan areas to supply them with fresh milk. Based on data from Table 2,

which province in Canada has the largest absolute number of dairy farms and also a large proportion of all its farms devoted to dairying?

Which province has the second largest number of dairy farms, but is not so specialized in dairy production? These two provinces are Canada's most populous. Use an atlas to identify four large cities in these two provinces that would provide good markets for milk and other dairy products. Put dots for these, with their names, on your map. Vancouver, B.C., Calgary and Edmonton, Alberta, and Winnipeg, Manitoba are other large cities with "milk sheds" nearby. Locate and label these on your map.

From a map of world climate zones, obtain the name for the type of climate that predominates in southern Ontario and Quebec.

More acres of "total hay and fodder crops" are planted in Ontario and Quebec than of any other crop. How does this fact fit with dairying?

7. The distribution of farms specializing in beef cattle is different from that of dairy farms. What are the top four provinces in number of beef cattle operations?

If you compare the number of beef cattle farms to the number of dairy farms in each province, which three provinces most strongly emphasize the former?

Use your textbook or atlas to find out how the climate in this part of Canada differs from that to the east (and the west).

How are large farm size, beef cattle, and the climate you identified connected?

8. Saskatchewan, Alberta, and Manitoba have 98 percent of all Canada's farms in this category, and Saskatchewan alone has more than two thirds. What is this major specialty of the Prairie Provinces? Other important crops in this region include canola (the "can" in canola comes from the "Can" in Canada), barley, and oats. On a world map of soils, you will see that the prairie lands of Canada and the United States share with two other major world regions the same kind of grasslands soils that are well-suited to growing the crop you identified above. What are these two other places?

9. Three provinces account for 84 percent of Canada's fruit or vegetable farms. Which provinces are these? What is the fourth-ranked province in this category? Like dairying, the locations of these farms are influenced both by markets and by climate. Some products of these farms are perishable and so are attracted to locations near their customers. Much of Canada has too harsh a climate for fruits and vegetables, so their farmers have to seek out the most southerly possible locations, protected valleys, or lands along large bodies of water that serve to moderate winter temperatures and prolong growing seasons. Find out from your textbook, atlas, or another source where each of the following Canadian fruit/vegetable districts is located: the Annapolis-Cornwallis Valley; the valley of the St. Lawrence River; the Niagara Plain; the Okanagan Valley; the lower valley of the Fraser River. Write down the province in which each is found.

Chapter 9, Geography for Life Activities, continued

10. Label dairy, beef cattle, wheat, and fruit/vegetable areas of Canada on your map. Indicate also potatoes, an important specialty crop for New Brunswick, Newfoundland, and Prince Edward Island.

Table 1. Selected Data on Canadian Agriculture, 1996.						
Province	Total Land Area	Land Area in Farms	% of Land in Farms	Average Farm Size	Gross Farm Receipts (GFR)	% of Canada's GFR
Alberta	157,710	51,964	32.9	881	7,911,131	24.5
British Columbia	220,584	6,249	_____	286	1,839,217	_____
Manitoba	135,340	19,017	_____	784	2,970,071	_____
New Brunswick	17,685	954	_____	280	325,684	_____
Newfoundland	91,832	108	_____	146	75,867	_____
Nova Scotia	13,057	1,056	_____	237	384,333	_____
Ontario	226,529	13,880	_____	206	7,778,476	_____
Prince Edward Island	1,398	655	_____	296	349,196	_____
Quebec	335,521	8,540	_____	237	4,972,518	_____
Saskatchewan	140,877	65,654	_____	1,152	5,623,863	_____
Canada (10 provinces)	1,340,533	168,076	_____	608	32,230,356	_____

NOTE. Land area is expressed in 1000s of acres. Farm size is expressed in acres. Gross Farm Recipts (GFR) are expressed in 1000s of Canadian dollars.

Table 2. Number of Farms by Type and Province in Canada, 1996

Province	Beef Cattle	Grain & Oil-seed	Wheat	Misc. Spec.	Dairy	Field Crop	Fruit or Vegetable	Hog	Live-Stock	Combi-nation	Poultry & Egg	Total
Alberta	24,718	10,343	5,243	4,794	1,418	3,825	163	1,149	1,448	998	527	54,626
British Columbia	4,413	240	119	4,784	1,184	1,621	3,431	206	623	476	925	18,022
Manitoba	7,018	6,110	3,407	1,334	946	1,248	150	946	489	407	401	22,456
New Brunswick	758	22	3	542	399	449	315	75	54	79	79	2,775
Newfoundland	28	0	0	139	63	39	162	13	15	60	54	573
Nova Scotia	912	6	2	868	502	176	751	93	76	101	113	3,600
Ontario	14,172	12,250	466	8,547	8,320	4,965	3,444	2,677	2,030	1,330	1,686	59,887
Prince Edward Island	592	39	9	125	337	528	110	103	93	42	37	2,015
Quebec	5,968	2,639	85	6,260	10,730	2,004	2,089	2,315	376	608	832	33,906
Saskatch.	8,952	19,928	20,192	1,322	512	1,390	99	486	1,013	906	179	54,979
Total	67,531	51,577	29,526	28,715	24,411	16,245	10,714	8,063	6,217	5,007	4,833	252,839

Notes: Farms with less than $2,500 in Gross Farm Receipts are not included. "Grain and Oilseed" excludes wheat. "Misc. Spec." = Miscellaneous Specialty. "Field Crop" excludes grain and oilseed.

Source: Statistics Canada. 1996 Census of Agriculture. At www.statcan.ca.

ACTIVITY (10)   Geography for Life Activities

National Geography Standard 4   **Mexican Tourism**

*The first mass tourist destinations in the world were the seaside resorts of Great
Britain. Before about 1870, leisure travel had been restricted to the upper
classes. With better wages, regular holidays, and affordable travel provided by
the train, more and more people could leave home for reasons of pleasure. Since
that time, the growth and spread of tourism have been phenomenal. In 1998,
the World Tourism Organization reported more than 625 million international
tourist arrivals and $445 billion in tourist receipts. Some sources rank tourism
as the largest single industry in the world today. This activity examines the
growth of tourism in Mexico.*

Tourism touches geography at many points. There are ever-shifting spatial distributions of
tourist destinations and facilities. There are complex patterns of movement (of both people and money). There are tourist regions. There are major environmental and cultural
impacts. There is a great deal of place promotion. All of these aspects interest geographers.

Tourism in Mexico was stimulated in the late 1930s by completion of the Pan-American
Highway from Laredo, Texas to Mexico City. Since that time, except for the World War II
years (1941–1945), the number of foreign visitors has increased yearly. Mexican tourism
benefited from the booming post-war economy, the development of the jet engine, and
proximity to the United States, the largest tourism sending market in the world.

Mexico as a Tourist Destination

Since 1970 Mexico has become one of the most popular tourist destinations in the world.
By the 1990s it was the number one Latin American country for tourist arrivals, and 40
percent of all international travelers to Latin America went to Mexico. Until recently,
Mexico also ranked number one in international tourist receipts among all Less Developed
Countries (China has since surpassed it). In 1998 Mexico drew almost 20 million foreign
visitors who spent over $7.8 billion. (These figures exclude excursionists who cross the
border but do not stay overnight. Excursionists are vital to the economies of border cities
such as Tijuana and Ciudad Juárez.) This number was up from 14 million a decade earlier.

Tourism is important to the Mexican economy. In recent years, tourism has ranked as
Mexico's second- or third-largest source of foreign currency (exports of petroleum and
manufactured goods are the other top-ranking sources). In 1998 the World Travel and
Tourism Council reported that nearly 3 million Mexicans worked in jobs related to
tourism, accounting for nearly 12 percent of the overall Mexican economy. Domestic
tourism contributes to these numbers; it has a geography all its own.

The predominant kind of tourism aimed at foreign visitors to Mexico today is large-
scale mass tourism centered around beaches. The Mexican government has participated
actively in the development of this kind of tourism. In the early 1970s the government's
Banco de México spent three years studying ways to increase Mexican exports. The bank
decided to emphasize tourism by planning and creating five new tourist resorts. These

were Cancún on the east coast of theYucatán Peninsula; Ixtapa north of Acapulco in the state of Guerrero; Los Cabos and Loreto on the Baja California peninsula; and Huatulco in the southern state of Oaxaca (see the map on the next page). Among the reasons for these particular choices was their location in poor areas of the country, where it was hoped that tourism investment would stimulate additional regional development.

The Results of Tourism Developmemt

Cancún took off first, attracting about 100,000 foreign visitors in 1975; by 1991 the number had shot up to 1.9 million. By the mid-1980s one-tenth of all visitors to Mexico went to Cancún, and by 1986 more people went there than to the long-established port and resort city of Acapulco. In 1989 Cancún even surpassed the Federal District (Mexico City) to become the single most popular Mexican destination for international tourists. Today Cancún is the nucleus of what is sometimes called the "Mayan Riviera."

Ixtapa-Zihuatanejo began to attract foreign tourists about the same time as Cancún, and in the early 1980s Los Cabos and Loreto followed (although the latter project was later severely curtailed). Foreign visitors began to visit Huatulco about 1987. By the early 1990s these five tourist "growth poles" were attracting one-quarter of all international tourists to Mexico. The impact on the older resort areas along the "Mexican Riviera" (between Mazatlán and Puerto Escondido) in the face of this new competition has varied. For example, Acapulco has suffered somewhat, while Puerto Vallarta has continued to thrive.

The pursuit of mass beach tourism has not been without controversy. Established residents of areas targeted for development were not invited to participate in the planning of the new resorts. Many resented being displaced by posh hotels, luxury condominiums, and golf courses for wealthy *norteamericanos*. The environment has paid a high price for the developments in terms of pollution and habitat destruction (although at Huatulco, more than half of the area is to remain as open space, in part in response to growing environmental concerns).

Many hotels in the new resort areas are part of large foreign (especially American) chains. One negative result for the Mexican economy of these chains is that profits are "leaking" out of the country. But the move toward transnational corporations was intentional; it was thought that Americans would not be attracted to the resorts without recognizable brand names to give them confidence. All of the resorts offer a stark contrast in quality of life between wealthy foreign tourists and the low-paid workers who serve them. The ranks of sparkling beachfront accommodations hide large areas of poverty and poor housing. Finally, there are concerns about the overall impact of large numbers of foreigners on local cultures, such as that of the Maya in the Yucatán Peninsula.

Fine-Tuning the Tourist Industry

There have been efforts in recent years to offer alternative destinations and types of tourism in Mexico. Many people come not only to bake on the beach but to visit Mexico's famed archeological treasures such as Monte Albán and Chichén Itzá. Others come to see the

Chapter 10, Geography for Life Activities, continued

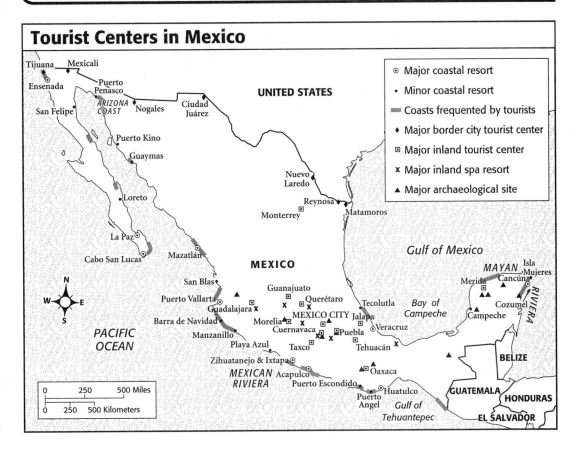

amazing giant that is Mexico City. The colonial architectural legacy of many cities—for example, Pátzcuaro (Michoacán) or Guanajuato—also appeals. Other people come to experience what they can of living Indian cultures, such as at San Cristóbal de las Casas in Chiapas. Still others are interested in Mexico's natural wonders, from Copper Canyon in dry Chihuahua to the Sian Ka'an Biosphere Reserve in tropical Quintana Roo. Ecotourism, with its promise of low environmental impact, is of growing importance. Various types of Mexican tourist destinations are displayed on the map above.

You Are the Geographer

Use the map and other resources, including your textbook and a guidebook or travel-related Web sites, to pick a tourist destination in Mexico that interests you. (If you have trouble getting started, begin with the capital city of one of Mexico's 31 states.) Your job is to produce a brochure for visitors to that place. It should include information on the usual tourist sites in the area, but it should also contain general descriptive information. For example, information on the local climate, plants and animals, and topography (physical geography) should appear in your brochure.

There should be some human geography too. What are the place's characteristic types of farming or industry? What ethnic groups live in the area? What are important local foods? In other words, the tourist who picks up your brochure should have a better sense of ordinary life in the area after reading it, not just knowledge of tourist highlights.

Chapter 10, Geography for Life Activities, continued

Your brochure should include a sketch map (your choice of subject, scale, etc.) and pictures. Sources of information include your textbook, atlases, guidebooks to Mexico (your teacher may have these available), encyclopedias, and Web sites. In this case, commercial (as well as government or organizational) Web sites will be useful, as you can see what kinds of tourist experiences are being offered.

ACTIVITY 11   Geography for Life Activities

National Geography Standard 10   **The Geography of Caribbean Music**

Many aspects of music are suitable for geographical study. To begin with, there are many "where" questions. Where are different music genres popular? Where are different kinds of instruments made and played? Where do people in different parts of the world go to listen to music? This activity examines the geography of Caribbean music.

Many music geographers do origin and diffusion studies. They identify the hearth, or place of origin, of a musical style or some other aspect of music and then trace its spread from that place. Music diffuses in a variety of ways. People carry it with them when they migrate (relocation diffusion), when they share CDs (contagious diffusion), and when they sit in a small town and listen to big city radio station (hierarchical diffusion). New musical genres can arise when different musical traditions are brought together through diffusion.

Particular places or regions often come to be associated with certain kinds of music. Some geographers are interested in how music contributes to a place's identity or to the identity of a group of people within a place. How do sound and lyrics give voice to a place or to the people in it?

The Roots of Caribbean Music

The Caribbean region has given rise to a number of original and dynamic musical genres. Music occupies an especially esteemed position in Caribbean societies. The richness of the music scene is tied to the cultural diversity present in the region. Influences from every continent can be found. There are rural and urban, peasant and elite elements. Local musical traditions mix with international styles. Fusions of two or more distinct traditions are called *syncretisms*. Religious and linguistic syncretisms, as well as musical ones, are important in the Caribbean.

The roots of Caribbean music are in the musical cultures of Africa and Europe. The European colonial powers—Dutch, English, French, and Spanish—imported African slaves to the Caribbean to work on plantations. The slaves came from a variety of African regions and cultures. Nonetheless, it is possible to identify some common features of the musical traditions they brought with them.

Collective participation in music-making was the norm. There were musical soloists and specialists, but everyone took part, by singing, clapping, dancing, or playing instruments. This situation meant that musical skills were widely developed.

A second feature of traditional African music is its emphasis on rhythm. The rhythmic complexity of African music is rarely matched in Western folk or classical music. Rhythm is often the basis for distinguishing among different genres of Afro-Caribbean music. It is often the musical feature that most commands the attention of performers and listeners.

A third feature is vocal call and response, a common device in African music. A related feature is what Peter Manual, in his book *Caribbean Currents,* calls "cellular structure." A short musical cell is repeated over and over, sometimes with variations; other elements, such as a narrative text, are added. These pieces have an open-ended, additive quality. These and other elements of African music did not survive to the same degree in all parts of the Caribbean. Why not? Some scholars note that the Spanish and French colonists were more tolerant of African cultural practices than were the British and Dutch. Perhaps this was linked to the fact that Roman Catholicism was more compatible with African religions, than was Protestantism. Also, it was easier for slaves to buy their freedom in Spanish and French colonies than elsewhere. Communities of free blacks could play their traditional music unhindered.

A final reason for the uneven pattern of African musical retention is that the slave trade with Africa lasted longer in some places than others. In British colonies, the last slaves came from Africa in 1804. In Cuba, they were still arriving in the 1870s. This means that Cuba continued to receive fresh infusions of African culture for much longer. The situation was different yet in Haiti, a French colony. The African slave trade ended there early (in the 1790s). However, a revolution sent the Europeans packing. Thus neo-African music and other cultural expressions could flourish without hindrance.

European Influences

European colonial contributions to Caribbean music are diverse. They include classical music, but more importantly, folk and popular songs and dances of the period. These include sailors' chanteys, church hymns, military marches, and social dances (the quadrille, mazurka, waltz, and contradance). Fiddles, guitars, and fifes were the common early European instruments; many others came along later. Some music introduced by the Europeans had aspects in common with that brought over by the Africans. Examples include the complex rhythms of some Spanish dance music, the use of call and response in some Protestant hymns, and festive music accompanying seasonal carnivals.

The mixing together of European and African musical elements in the Caribbean has created a large number of musical syncretisms or creoles. (The word *creole* is often applied to people of black and white mixed ancestry. The term is also applied to languages that begin as pidgins but evolve into full-blown languages.) It was most often lower-class Afro-Caribbeans who initiated the musical mixing. European-oriented elites tended to denounce it. However, in many cases the syncretisms have worked their way up the social hierarchy, have become more sophisticated, and have been adopted by all classes. As the decades of the 1970s went by and as a result of "black is beautiful" movements, more and more people in the Caribbean appreciated the African sources of their national styles of music. Now these national musical styles have gone international. Millions of migrants from the Caribbean have carried them abroad, and new influences from around the world have entered the Caribbean. Cuba, Puerto Rico, the Dominican Republic, Haiti, Jamaica, Trinidad, and Martinique and Guadeloupe each have their own distinctive musical genres.

Cuban Contributions

As *World Music, The Rough Guide* notes, "Forget sugar, cigars, and rum—music is Cuba's greatest export." Cuban musicians invented the rumba, the mambo, the cha-cha, the danzón, and the habanera, all musical genres and dances that traveled around the world. *Son* is the predominant force in Cuban song and dance. It emerged as early as the 1880s during the struggle for the abolition of slavery. Often played by a sextet or septet, *son* combines complex African rhythms and Latin harmonic and melodic elements. The lyrics were originally improvised. They follow an old Spanish verse form called the *décima*. Often *son* lyrics express romantic themes, but they can also address social and political issues (including anti-American sentiment). So can the lyrics of *nuevas trovas* (new ballads), which emerged in the 1970s and built on Cuba's old *trova* (ballad) and *canción* (song) traditions. They provide commentary on life in a revolutionary society. People often go to the local *casa de la trova* to hear Cuban music. These are informal places, encouraged by the Cuban government, for playing and listening to music. New York City and Miami are also important places for Cuban music.

Elements of African music and religion are less prominent in Puerto Rico than in Cuba. This is tied to the fact that slavery was less widespread in Puerto Rico than in Cuba (the main crops in Puerto Rico during the Spanish period were tobacco and coffee, which require less labor than the sugarcane that became so dominant in Cuba). *Jíbaros,* the island's white farmers (peasants, not big landowners) were long viewed as embodiments of Puerto Rican identity. *Jíbaro* music, including the *seis* and the *aguinaldo*, became an important symbol of island culture. The instruments and harmony of these forms are Spanish, but they incorporate African-derived and Cuban rhythms. The lyrics comment on many aspects of Puerto Rican experience. In the 1970s, under American rule, many *jíbaros* lost their land and migrated to cities (including New York City). Many lyrics lament the loss of a rural way of life and the destruction of tradition and nature. Other forms of Puerto Rican music are the *plena* and the *bomba*.

Offshoots of Caribbean Music

In the Latin barrios of New York City, Cuban and Puerto Rican music mixed with big-band jazz to give birth to *salsa*. From its emergence in the 1970s, *salsa* spread throughout the Caribbean and Latin America. There are many national and local varieties. References to elements of Caribbean and Latin American Afro-Catholic religions are common. Some salsa numbers tell stories of life in the barrio.

The Dominican Republic's national musical forms are the *merengue* and the *bacháta*. One of the signatures of traditional *merengue* was use of the accordion, which was introduced to the country by German immigrants. The *bacháta* grows out of the bitter experience of the shantytowns of Santo Domingo, the capital city of the Dominican Republic.

There are important links between Haiti's syncretic religion, voodoo, and its music and dance. *Rara* music, for example, is associated with street celebrations held after Carnival (which precedes the Christian season of Lent). Other Haitian styles include the *mereng, konpa dirèk* (direct rhythm), and *vodou-jazz*.

On the French Antillean islands Martinique and Guadaloupe, traditional drum and vocal music associated with festivals and strings and reeds associated with the *biguine* combined in the 1950s and 1960s to become a style called *cadence. Cadence* in turn meta-morphosed into *zouk,* described in the *Rough Guide* as the Caribbean's "first really hi-tech dance music." Paris became the major overseas center for zouk music, which also has influenced popular music in parts of Africa.

Although Jamaica started life as a Spanish colony, it became British in 1670. Its folk and religious music shows African, British, Irish, and Spanish influences. The music of various Protestant denominations has left it mark. Jamaican styles that have emerged since the 1950s include ska, rock steady, reggae, dub, dancehall, and ragga. An important facet of Jamaican music is its ties to Rastafarianism, a church that looks forward to the return of New World blacks to Africa. The hundreds of thousands of West Indians in Britain have made Birmingham and London the foreign capitals of Jamaican music.

Trinidad is the home of calypso, derived from the *gayup,* a West African communal work song. The island experienced Spanish, French, and British colonial eras, and calypso shows all these influences. There are important links to Carnival festivities and proces-sions, as elsewhere in the Caribbean. Lyrics are important in calypso; in fact in its early days, calypsonians were the newspapers of Trinidad. Lots of political commentary finds its way into calypso. A hi-tech version of calypso that shows influences from other popu-lar 1970s genres is called soca. The Trinidadians have their own national instrument, the steel drum or pan, made from a 45-gallon oil drum. Steel bands are largely amateur. East Indians are an important ethnic group on Trinidad, brought there by the British to work on the plantations. Their traditional folk songs, called *tan,* have lately been joined by sim-pler, catchier Indo-Caribbean tunes called chutney. The lyrics of *tan* and chutney are in Hindi.

You Are the Geographer

Divide your class into groups, with one group each assigned to prepare an oral presenta-tion on the music of Cuba, Puerto Rico, the Dominican Republic, Haiti, Jamaica, Trinidad, and Martinique/Guadaloupe. Your presentation should include: (1) examples of the music for your audience to hear, (2) a map of your island(s) or country that includes places rele-vant to its music geography (this could be a poster or an overhead transparency), (3) a description of the various cultural influences on the music, (4) comments on how and where the music has spread via outmigration, and (5) a discussion of song lyrics that say something about life on the island or in the neighborhoods of its people living abroad (some liner notes provide English translations).

Name _____ Class _____ Date _____

Geography for Life Activities

National Geography Standard 12   **Latin American Urbanization**

> *South America is the most urbanized continent in the world. This means that a greater share (79 percent) of its people live in towns and cities than do the people of any other continent. As recently as 1925, only 33 percent of South Americans lived in towns and cities. In 1950 there were 110 million people in South America of which 46 million lived in urban places. Currently, there are 350 million South Americans, of which 277 million are city-dwellers. That means that the cities of the continent have added 231 million people during the past half-century, as many people as there are now in Great Britain, Germany, France, Belgium, Austria, and Switzerland combined. Yet unlike those places, South America is not wealthy.*

This activity is all about doing the work of a geographer, from analyzing your data to mapping your results.

You Are the Geographer

1. As you can see from Table 1 near the end of this activity, not all South American countries are equally urbanized. Primate city systems are those in which the largest city is extremely dominant. A primate city has a high share of its country's population and is much larger than the country's second largest city. A primate city also concentrates in one place a country's power, wealth, and cultural and economic resources. This concentration is often seen as a problem, because other parts of the country remain underdeveloped and without access to many kinds of opportunities.

Table 1 lists urban areas in South America that have one million or more inhabitants (plus second-ranking cities for Chile, Paraguay, and Uruguay, even though these cities have fewer than one million people). Calculate two different measures of primacy for each of the 10 major countries in the table (skip the Guianas). First, figure out what share of the national population is captured by the largest city (for example, Buenos Aires has 34 percent of Argentina's population). Put your results on the line provided. Second, figure out how many times larger the largest city is than the second largest (for example, Buenos Aires is nine times the size of Córdoba). Put these results in the line provided.

Which three South American city systems have the highest degree of primacy and which three have the lowest, according to the first measure? Which have the highest degree of primacy and which three have the lowest, according to the second measure? What factors do you think might contribute to the development of a primate city? (Hint: consider what kinds of political and economic systems these countries had as colonies and continue to have today. Also think about country size.)

2. To see the arrangement of South America's large urban populations, you will map them using graduated circle symbols and the base map provided at the end of this

Chapter 12, Geography for Life Activities, continued

activity. For each city, the area of the circle will be proportional to its population size. For example, Belo Horizonte's population is twice as large as Fortaleza's, so the area of the former's circle will be twice that of the latter's.

Since the area of a circle is πr^2, and since π is constant, the method of construction is to find the square roots of the data and then construct circles with radii (and diameters) proportional to the square roots. (Research into how people actually perceive circular areas has shown that they underestimate the sizes of larger circles compared to smaller ones. So when professional cartographers or computer-mapping programs construct graduated circles they adjust the relative sizes to take this into account.)

Use your calculator to find the square root of each city population. Put these in a column. Decide how small your smallest circle is going to be; probably no smaller than .25 inch in diameter. Concepción, Chile, has the smallest population you will be mapping, so let's make its diameter .25 inch. Its population is 363,000, the square root of which is 602.5. So what size would the largest circle be? (Is is always a good idea to check this out before proceeding further, since if it proves to be gigantic, some other cartographic technique may need to be used. Or if it is too small, compared to the base map, you may want to make the smallest circle larger.) São Paulo has 17,755,000 residents. Its square root is 4213.7. Let x stand for the diameter of its circle. Then,

$$\frac{602.5}{.25} = \frac{4213.7}{x} \qquad so, x = \frac{.25(4213.7)}{602.5} \qquad x = 1.75$$

So the diameter of your largest circle will be 1.75 inches. This is about right, given the size of your base map. Now calculate the diameters of all the other circles. You may want to divide up this work so that each person only has to calculate a few.

Use the outline map of South America provided at the end of this activity. You will need a compass to construct your circles. In order to assign the right circle to the right dot on your base map, you will also need a reference map of South America. Some of the circles on your map will overlap, and that is fine. Cartographers deal with this problem by leaving the circles transparent or by putting the smaller circles "on top of" the larger ones. Label each circle with its city name and also add country names. Give your map a title. It also needs a legend, which should consist of a set of several circles of different sizes, each with the population it represents. You might want to look in an atlas for examples of graduated circle maps to see how they handle overlapping circles and legends.

Now look at the pattern on your map. Where are South America's big cities found in abundance? Where are they scarce? Use what you know about the continent's physical geography and history of colonialism to explain the patterns you see.

Table 1. Populations of Countries and Cities Over One Million

Country City	Population	Country City	Population
Argentina (90% urban)	37,500,000	**Ecuador** (62%)	12,900,000
Buenos Aires	12,560,000	Guayaquil	2,393,000
% Total Population	_____	% Total Population	_____
Relative Size	_____	Relative Size	_____
Córdoba	1,434,000	Quito	1,754,000
Rosario	1,278,000	**French Guiana** (79%)	200,000
Bolivia (63% urban)	8,500,000	**Guyana** (36%)	700,000
La Paz	1,480,000	**Paraguay** (52%)	5,700,000
		Asuncion	1,262,000
% Total Population	_____	% Total Population	_____
Relative Size	_____		
Santa Cruz	1,065,000	Relative Size	_____
Brazil (81% urban)	171,800,000	Villarrica	30,000
São Paulo	17,755,000	**Peru** (72%)	26,100,000
		Lima	7,443,000
% Total Population	_____	% Total Population	_____
Relative Size	_____		
Rio de Janeiro	10,582,000	Relative Size	_____
Belo Horizonte	4,170,000	Arequipa	1,000,000
Salvador	2,303,000	**Suriname** (69%)	400,000
Fortaleza	2,098,000	**Uruguay** (92%)	3,400,000
Brasilia	1,990,000	Montevideo	1,360,000
Curitiba	1,584,000		
Recife	1,378,000	% Total Population	_____
Pôrto Alegre	1,314,000		
Manaus	1,255,000	Relative Size	_____
Belém	1,187,000	Salto	80,000
Goiânia	1,056,000	**Venezuela** (87%)	24,600,000
Chile (86% urban)	15,400,000	Caracas	3,673,000
Santiago	5,538,000		
		% Total Population	_____
% Total Population	_____		
		Relative Size	_____
Relative Size	_____	Maracaibo	1,901,000
Concepción	363,000	Valencia	1,893,000
Colombia (71% urban)	43,100,000	Baraquisimeto	1,000,000
Bogotá	6,288,000		
% Total Population	_____		
Relative Size	_____		
Medillín	2,951,000		
Cali	2,710,000		
Barranquilla	1,736,000		

Name _____ Class _____ Date _____

ACTIVITY 13   Geography for Life Activities

National Geography Standard 14   **Evaluating European Forests**

*Forests are important for many reasons. Forests provide valuable wood and
nonwood products, offer recreational and spiritual opportunities, protect soil
and water resources, and provide habitat for plants and animals. This exercise
looks at how people can better understand forest management.*

Maps of Europe's natural vegetation reveal that, prior to human modification, nearly all
of the continent was wooded. Much of Sweden and Finland in the subarctic climate zone
was covered in evergreen needleleaf trees known as the boreal forest. Pine, fir, and spruce
were common. In the marine west coast climate zone of northwestern Europe, forest
could be predominantly needleleaf, broadleaf, or mixed. Important broadleaf species
were oak, ash, and beech. Farther east, in the humid continental climate zone, forests
were mixed or broadleaf. In the Mediterranean parts of Europe, a scrub woodland of
hardleaved evergreen trees and shrubs prevailed. Areas of natural grasslands or tundra
were relatively small.

Forests have become newsworthy recently. This interest relates to the forest's function
as a carbon store. Humans are putting huge amounts of carbon dioxide into the atmosphere, mostly by burning fossil fuels. Many scientists think that increased carbon dioxide
and other greenhouse gases are contributing to global warming. Since forests store carbon, maintaining and expanding them offsets the carbon being put into the atmosphere.

You Are the Geographer

In this exercise, you will learn more about Europe's forest resources. Table 1 at the end of
this activity provides data on Europe's forests, along with data on other world regions
where temperate and boreal forests are found. Table 2 displays data on individual
European countries. Use the information in these tables to answer the following
questions.

1. Europe has about as much forested land as _____, but

only about two-fifths as much as _____ and one-fifth as much

as _____.

2. Calculate the percentage of each region's forests that are judged "undisturbed by
humans," "semi-natural," and "plantations." Put these percentages in the spaces
provided in the table. How do Europe's forests compare to those of the other three
temperate forest regions in this regard?

_____

_____

_____

3. Some forest is not available for wood supply (FNAWS) because it is protected or it would be too costly to harvest (generally due to remote location). Calculate the percentage of each region's FNAWS and enter these figures in the table. Which region has the smallest share of its forested land protected by law or economic situation?

_____

4. Calculate the percentage of each region's forests that are in public ownership and enter these figures in the table. How does Europe compare to the other regions?

_____

5. Calculate how may hectares of forest land each region has per capita and enter these figures in the table. Explain, using these figures, why Europeans have been reluctant to agree to the proposal that carbon dioxide emissions can be "paid for" by having extensive forest resources.

_____

_____

6. Which five European countries have the greatest absolute extent of forested land?

_____

_____

7. Which five European countries have the greatest share of their land forested? What geographic characteristics do these countries share?

_____

_____

8. Which five countries have the most forested land per capita? Which five have the least? Are these the same countries that you listed in questions 8 and 9?

_____

_____

9. Which five countries have the greatest proportions of their forest judged to be "undisturbed by humans"? What geographic characteristics do these countries have in common? How many countries have no undisturbed forest?

_____

_____

Chapter 13, Geography for Life Activities, continued

10. Which five countries have the greatest proportions of their forest in plantations? What geographic characteristics do these countries have in common?

_____

_____

Table 1. Selected Temperate Forest Data by World Region					
	Europe*	Former Soviet Union	North America	Australia/ New Zealand/ Japan	Total
Forest Land	175,828	855,740	461,904	188,891	1,682,363
Undisturbed by humans	7,036	750,856	143,157	23,496	924,545
As a percentage of all forest land	____	____	____	____	____
Semi-natural	156,703	82,305	305,060	152,119	696,187
As a percentage of all forest land	____	____	____	____	____
Plantations	12,089	22,579	13,687	13,276	61,631
As a percentage of all forest land	____	____	____	____	____
FNAWS	27,000	309,000	138,000	147,000	621,000
FNAWS as a percentage of all forest land	____	____	____	____	____
Forest Land in Public Ownership	79,401	855,740	291,824	129,945	1,356,910
Public forest land as a percentage of all forest land	____	____	____	____	____
Population of region (in 1000s)	585,075	284,112	304,591	148,786	1,322,564
Hectares of forest land per capita	____	____	____	____	____
Average annual change in forest extent	+500	-520	+590	+40	+610

NOTE: Data are expressed in thousands of hectares. One hectare = 2.47 acres. FNAWS = Forests not available for wood supply.
*Includes Turkey, Israel Estonia, Latvia, and Lithuania.
Source: United Nations Economic Commission for Europe and Food and Agriculture Organization of the United Nations. 2000. *Forest Resources of Europe, CIS, North America, Australia, Japan and New Zealand.* Geneva Timber and Forest Study Papers, No. 17. New York and Geneva: United Nations.

Name _____ Class _____ Date _____

Table 2. Selected European Forest Data by Country

Country	Forest land (1,000 ha)	Percentage of land forested	Forest per capita (ha/cap)	Percentage of forest undisturbed by humans	Percentage of forest that is semi-natural	Percentage of forest that is plantations
Albania	1,030	37.3	0.33	8.2	81.9	9.9
Austria	3,840	47.6	0.47	0.9	99.1	0.0
Belgium	646	21.3	0.06	0.0	54.4	45.6
Bosnia and Herzegovina	2,276	44.9	0.62	0.0	97.5	2.5
Bulgaria	3,590	32.9	0.43	7.1	65.9	27.0
Croatia	1,775	31.7	0.40	0.1	97.2	2.6
Czech Republic	2,630	34.0	0.26	0.0	76.9	23.1
Denmark	445	10.5	0.08	0.1	23.4	76.5
Estonia	2,016	48.1	1.41	0.1	84.8	15.1
Finland	21,883	71.9	4.25	5.8	94.2	0.0
France	15,156	28.0	0.26	0.2	93.5	6.3
Germany	10,740	31.0	0.13	0.0	100.0	0.0
Greece	3,359	25.7	0.32	0.0	96.4	3.6
Hungary	1,811	19.9	0.18	0.0	92.5	7.5
Iceland	30	0.3	0.11	0.0	60.0	40.0
Ireland	591	8.6	0.16	0.2	0.0	99.8
Italy	9,857	33.5	0.17	0.1	98.6	1.3
Latvia	2,884	46.4	1.19	0.1	94.9	5.0
Lithuania	1,978	31.6	0.54	0.6	85.0	14.4
Luxembourg	86	33.3	0.20	0.0	100.0	0.0
Netherlands	339	10.0	0.02	0.0	70.5	29.5
Norway	8,710	28.4	1.97	2.9	93.7	3.4
Poland	8,942	29.4	0.23	1.6	97.9	0.4
Portugal	3,383	37.2	0.34	1.6	73.7	24.7
Romania	6,301	27.5	0.28	3.7	94.9	1.4
Slovakia	2,016	41.9	0.37	1.0	98.3	0.7
Slovenia	1,099	54.5	0.55	4.5	95.4	0.1
Spain	13,509	27.0	0.34	0.0	85.9	14.1
Sweden	27,264	66.8	3.07	16.1	81.8	2.1
Switzerland	1,173	30.0	0.16	0.6	99.1	0.3
The FYR of Macedonia	906	35.8	0.45	0.0	96.7	3.3
United Kingdom	2,469	10.2	0.04	0.0	31.3	68.7
Yugoslavia	2,894	28.6	0.27	0.1	98.5	1.4
United States	217,333	23.7	0.79	8.8	84.9	6.3

NOTE: 1 hectare (ha) = 2.47 acres.

Source: United Nations Economic Commission for Europe and Food and Agriculture Organization of the United Nations. 2000. *Forest Resources of Europe, CIS, North America, Australia, Japan and New Zealand*. Geneva Timber and Forest Study Papers, No. 17. New York and Geneva: United Nations.

Name _____ Class _____ Date _____

National Geography Standard 3   **Linking Denmark**

*Connections are of great interest to geographers. How well connected a place is
to other places plays a big role in determining its character. Some of the most
dramatic changes in places occur when they become newly connected or more
efficiently connected to other places. In this exercise we consider how Denmark's
geography has been altered through the strengthening of connections.*

Once the railroad linked the American West to the eastern states, the processes of settlement and development were accelerated. The West developed large cities, major industries, and regions of intensive market agriculture. When airplanes became commonplace,
tropical islands such as Hawaii were made accessible to tourists. The end result was an
economic, social, and ecologic transformation. Conversely, places that do not become
better connected to other places tend to remain poor economically. Many economic
development programs around the world include projects to improve transportation
linkages.

Denmark, at 16,639 square miles, is about the size of New Hampshire and Vermont
combined. Unlike these two states, it is highly fragmented (see the map at the end of this
activity). The Jutland Peninsula accounts for over half of Denmark's area, and about 2
million of its 5.3 million people. The rest of the country consists of an archipelago of
over 400 islands. Today, 80 of these islands are inhabited, some two dozen fewer than
were inhabited in 1900. The most populous islands are Zealand with 2.2 million people
and Fyn with nearly half a million.

Early Connections

Denmark's islands and mainland were connected mostly by boat before 1900, although
some very narrow straits were linked by bridges. Starting in 1872, the Danes pioneered
the use of short-sea rail ferries to interconnect their rail lines on the Jutland Peninsula,
Fyn, Zealand, and Falster-Lolland and to link with the railway systems of Sweden and
Germany. Roll-on-roll-off car ferries were introduced in 1930 on the Great Belt crossing.
By 1996 45 routes were operating using this system.

Also in the 1930s, the Danes used the latest technology to begin building bridges over
straits previously too wide to span. During the Depression, about a dozen large bridge
projects provided relief jobs for the unemployed. These bridges created an interconnected
west Denmark road and rail system on Jutland, the Jutland Islands (Thy, Mors, and
Vendsyssel, north of the peninsula), and Fyn and an east Denmark system on Zealand,
Lolland, and Falster. These two systems remained separated by the 11-mile-wide Great
Belt, which took an hour to cross by ferry, plus waiting time and long lines at peak
periods.

Chapter 14, Geography for Life Activities, *continued*

Recent Connections

Proposals to bridge the Great Belt were made as early as 1936. Severe ice conditions in 1947, which disrupted use of the ferries, brought renewed calls for a bridge. Finally, after years of study and technological progress, construction of the Great Belt Fixed Link began in 1988. The crossing consists of the (combined) low-level West Road/Rail Bridge between Fyn Island and the small island of Sprogo (greatly enlarged for the project) and the East Rail Tunnel and high-level East Road Bridge between Sprogo and Zealand Island. The crossing was opened to trains in 1997 and to automobiles in 1998. The configuration east of Sprogo was designed to keep the Great Belt open to ocean-going ships traveling to and from the Baltic Sea. Extra excavation of the seabed prevented the new structure from affecting water flow through the Great Belt between the Baltic Sea and the Kattegat, a key to maintaining the water quality and ecology of the Baltic.

Denmark opened a second major fixed link in 2000. A bridge (with a section of tunnel on the west end), carrying both train and automotive traffic, now connects Denmark and Sweden across the 4.8-mile-wide Øresund. Even though more crossings are being made than during the ferry era, fewer people than expected appear to be using the bridge. One reason is the cost, which is $26.40 per car one way. Regular commuters between Copenhagen and Malmö (Sweden's third largest city), which face each other across the Øresund Strait, pay a reduced amount.

Construction of the fixed link has led to recognition of an emerging Øresund Region. Malmö and Copenhagen newspapers produce a joint Øresund supplement each day. Various joint health, education, information technology, and cultural ventures have been launched across the international border. Tourist and business promotions are trying to give the region a unified personality. There is a lot of talk of transnational border regions emerging across Europe as the continent becomes more economically and physically integrated, partly due to the efforts of the European Union. Perhaps the Øresund will be one of the first to become a reality.

You Are the Geographer

Using the table and the map that follow, answer the following questions. Write your answers on a separate sheet of paper.

1. If transportation has improved since 1900 and places are better connected now than they were then, why have so many islands been abandoned?

2. What would be the effects of Denmark's (or any other country's) physical fragmentation on prices, levels of trade, and competition?

3. What big infrastructure projects similar to those in Denmark, also with major geographical and economic implications, were carried out in the United States during the Depression?

Chapter 14, Geography for Life Activities, continued

4. Calculate the percentage change in time savings made possible by the Great Belt fixed link for rail travel between Copenhagen and the seven regional cities listed in Table 1. Write your answers in the table.

5. Discuss the possible impacts of the construction of the Great Belt Fixed Link on the following places and sectors: eastern Fyn, including Odense, Denmark's fourth largest city; Copenhagen; southwest Zealand; north Jutland, including Ålborg; the ports of Rødbyhavn and Copenhagen; the ferry industry; the airlines; wholesalers.

6. More Swedes are crossing to Denmark than Danes to Sweden. What might be the reasons for that?

7. Identify and discuss what you know about a transnational border region involving the United States and one of its neighbors. Look in an atlas to see if you can find how these places are internally linked by their transportation systems.

Table 1
Travel Times between Copenhagen and Selected Regional Cities

Regional City	Train before Fixed Link	Train after Fixed Link	Percentage Change	Airplane
Odense	2h 30m	1h 15m	_____	1h 25m
Vejle	3h 10m	2h 00m	_____	1h 45m
Sønderborg (Als Is.)	5h 15m	3h 40m	_____	1h 20m
Esbjerg	4h 15m	2h 35m	_____	1h 30m
Århus	3h 55m	2h 40m	_____	1h 45m
Herning	5h 10m	2h 55m	_____	2h 00m
Ålborg	5h 50m	4h 10m	_____	1h 25m

Source: Knowles, Richard. 2000. The Great Belt Fixed Link and Denmark's Transition from Inter-island Sea to Land Transport. *Geography* 85(4): 345-354.

Chapter 14, Geography for Life Activities, continued

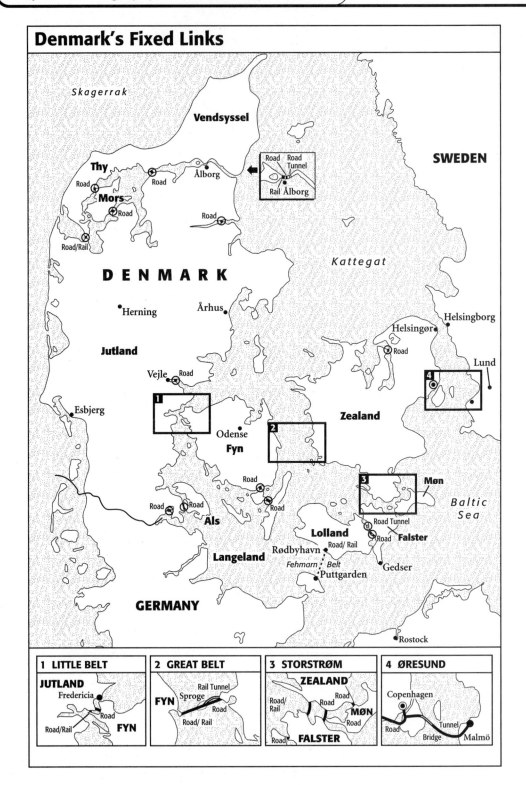

Denmark's Fixed Links

1 LITTLE BELT
2 GREAT BELT
3 STORSTRØM
4 ØRESUND

Name _____ Class _____ Date _____

Geography for Life Activities

National Geography Standard 6   **Symbols of a Reunited Berlin**

*Cultural geographers are interested in what places mean to people. What feel-
ings and ideas does a place convey? Does a particular place make you feel
proud, scared, ashamed, confident, bored? Does it symbolize neighborliness,
repression, indifference, freedom, holiness? How does a city or nation decide
which places or buildings are meaningful enough to preserve? In this exercise
you will read about the history of Berlin. At the end you will design a new open
space or structure to represent the reunited city.*

People in Berlin, Germany are giving a lot of attention to the questions posed above.
Berlin bears a particularly heavy load of painful memories. It is a city with a long and
colorful history. Each century has left buildings and monuments to illustrate its status
and growth. Efforts to create a new German identity are focused there.

The Early History of Berlin

The settlements of Berlin and Kölln were founded on opposite banks of the Spree River
in 1200. German settlers traded their grain for the wood and furs of Slavic hunters at this
river ford site. East-west and north-south trade routes passed through the twin towns.
Although they built a common town hall on the bridge between them in about 1345,
Berlin and Kölln remained independent for about another 100 years. At this point the
two cities were forced to submit to the rule of the Margrave and Prince-Elector of
Brandenburg (the region around Berlin), who was a member of the Hohenzollern family.
The new city seal showed the Hohenzollern eagle crushing the Berlin bear.

Over a period of five centuries, members of the Hohenzollern dynasty became dukes
of Prussia, then kings of Prussia, and finally emperors of a united Germany. In the
process, Berlin was transformed from a small trading town into an imperial metropolis. A
Hohenzollern palace was built in Kölln and occupied in 1451. It was rebuilt and remod-
eled several times in the following centuries. It survived World War I, was badly damaged
in World War II, and the ruins demolished in 1950. After the reunification of Berlin in
1990, there was serious discussion of rebuilding the royal palace, or at least its facade.
What would have been the meaning of such a project to contemporary Berliners?

Berlin in the 1600s to 1700s

In the 1600s, fortified walls were built to encompass Berlin, Kölln, and a third town. In
1709, those three towns plus two others were legally united into one city, Berlin. A quar-
ter-century later work began on a new city wall, enclosing a much-enlarged territory and
serving as a toll barrier. During this period the Hohenzollern rulers of Berlin became
increasingly powerful, acquiring huge additional territories. Most of these lands were to
the east of Brandenburg, including Silesia and Prussia (lands that today belong to Poland,
Russia, and Lithuania). Berlin became capital of the Prussian state and gained a large military population.

Berlin also became more cosmopolitan. Many foreigners, including Dutch craftsmen and merchants and skilled French and Bohemian textile workers were attracted to Berlin. Through the centuries, the position of Jews in Berlin was precarious. Sometimes they were tolerated for their financial and entrepreneurial skills; at other times, they were forced out.

Toward the end of the 1700s, a new customs (toll) wall was built. One of the wall's main gates, the Brandenburg Gate, was rebuilt in 1791. Napoleon so admired the sculpture on top (a goddess riding in a chariot pulled by four horses) that he had it removed to Paris. After Napoleon's defeat, the sculpture was returned. The Brandenburg Gate became a "Gate of Victory," symbolic of Prussian military success. It remained standing even after the wall was demolished in the 1860s. At least in part because of its location near the Berlin Wall (see below), the Brandenburg Gate has become the most well known symbol of Berlin.

Berlin in the 1800s

During the 1800s Berlin became a huge industrial metropolis. Its population grew from some 193,000 in 1815 to about a million in 1877. Textiles, porcelain, and metal products and later, locomotives, chemicals, and electrical motors were among the products of Berlin factories. The army's demands for supplies and arms stimulated industry. Financial institutions expanded. However, for ordinary people life was hard. Hunger, crowding, filth, disease, and death at a young age were commonplace in Berlin, as they were in other industrial cities of this period.

The 1800s also brought armed conflict and political change. The French army, under Napoleon, occupied Berlin from 1806 to 1813. After helping to defeat Napoleon, Prussia gained additional German territories. The year 1848 was a year of revolutionary activity in many parts of Europe including Berlin. Berliners revolted against the absolute power of the king, but they were unsuccessful. Prussia defeated Austria in 1866 and France in 1870, events commemorated by a 67-meter-tall Victory Column in Berlin. Under Prussian leadership, a unified German Empire (Deutches Reich) was proclaimed in January of 1871, with the King of Prussia becoming Kaiser (emperor). Berlin became the imperial capital.

One of the most important physical legacies from the Empire period is the Reichstag, built to house the German parliament. This building has recently been refurbished for the Bundestag, the national assembly of the reunited Germany. Berlin's famous subway system (the U-bahn) was also begun under the Empire.

The 1900s

Germany was on the losing side in World War I. During the war, Berliners suffered starvation, strikes, and political tensions. After the war, the Emperor fled Germany. A German Republic, usually called the Weimar Republic, was established in 1919 with Berlin as its capital.

Berlin in the 1920s was a place of cultural, economic, and political tensions. The arts flourished, including painting, literature, drama, music, and cinema. Modern architecture was nurtured in Berlin and left many important legacies. The tremendous cultural productivity of Berlin was brought up short when the American stock market crashed in 1929

Chapter 15, Geography for Life Activities, continued

and a deep depression followed. Voices on both the political right (the Nazis) and the political left (the Communists) used the crisis to criticize the moderate Weimar government. Worsening economic conditions in the early 1930s helped bring the Nazis to power.

Berlin became the capital of Hitler's Third Reich, even though Hitler hated the city. Twelve years of Nazi rule, including six years of war, left countless places in Berlin stained by memories of the terrible events that happened there. Years of bombardment could not erase these memories, although they reduced much of the city to rubble.

At the end of the war, different sectors of both Germany and Berlin were occupied by the armed forces of the Soviet Union, France, Britain, and the United States. Ultimately, Germany was split in two. The Soviet-occupied eastern part became the German Democratic Republic (GDR), a communist country under Soviet control. The remainder became the Federal Republic of Germany (FRG), a democratic republic with a free-market economy.

Berlin, deep in GDR territory, was similarly split. Separate governments were elected in East Berlin and West Berlin. East Berlin became the capital of the GDR and West Berlin remained part of the FRG. Large numbers of East Germans began defecting to West Berlin. This flow was halted in 1961 when workers began sealing the perimeter of West Berlin. The structure that eventually replaced the first barbed wire fence came to be known as the Berlin Wall. It was no mere wall, however; it was a cleared space between walls, secured by observation towers, bright lights, barbed wire, tank barriers, and dog runs.

East Berliners were not allowed to approach the wall from their side. West Berliners covered many stretches of the wall on their side with graffiti messages. Many of these messages took aim at the inhumanity or absurdity of the wall. The Berlin Wall became the most well-known symbol of the Cold War. After nearly 30 years, a collapsing East German government opened it in 1989. Later most of the wall was dismantled.

The next year, East and West Germany were reunited, as were East and West Berlin. Berlin became an enormous construction zone. All kinds of previously severed links were put back together. Buildings to accommodate the federal government (West Germany's capital had been in Bonn) started to go up, as did new commercial and residential structures. Many old buildings were refurbished. None of this could be done, however, without examining the memories and ghosts that were disturbed by all this turmoil.

You Are the Geographer

Suppose you were hired by the Berlin government to design a place to commemorate the city's reunification. Work with a small group of other students to devise a good process to follow (public participation is essential). Make some preliminary sketches. Write about what images from the past, present, and future you would or would not incorporate and why. Obtain additional outside information or imagery (maps and photographs) as needed. Prepare and display the final design. After everyone in your class has a chance to study the designs, have a class discussion about them.

A REUNITED BERLIN
PRELIMINARY WORK

Name _____ Class _____ Date _____

Geography for Life Activities

National Geography Standard 9   **Migration to Southern Europe**

Migration is of central concern to many geographers. Through migration, places
are transformed. Both the places migrants leave (their origins) and the places
they arrive (their destinations) are affected by their moving. In this exercise you
will learn about the recent migration experiences of Southern Europe, particu-
larly Spain.

During the period 1950–2000, the countries of Southern Europe experienced what population geographers call a "migration turnaround." They switched from being countries of
emigration to countries of immigration.

During the first half of this period, millions of Southern Europeans, together with
Yugoslavs, Turks, and North Africans, went to work in France, West Germany, Belgium,
the Netherlands, and Switzerland. These guest workers, as they were called, filled the "3-
D" jobs—dirty, dangerous, and demanding—in Northern Europe's very fast-growing
economies. Many family members of these guest workers joined them. Then economic
recession and changes in the structure of the economy occurred, and the demand for
such workers fell. The streams of emigrants from Southern Europe slowed to a trickle,
and the numbers of return migrants (people coming back) increased. As emigration from
Southern Europe declined, immigration to Southern Europe began rising.

Changing Trends

Why have Spain and the other countries of Southern Europe become a more popular
destination for migrants? There are several interrelated reasons for this trend. Firstly,
Northern Europe has become harder to get into directly. Southern Europe is part way
there and acts as a "waiting room," especially for North African migrants.

Secondly, the economies of Southern Europe have developed to the level where local
workers are not supplying low-wage labor. This situation does not mean that there is no
unemployment. In fact, there are high rates of unemployment in the countries of
Southern Europe. But some unemployed people will not accept a 3-D–type job. Some
employers prefer immigrant employees who will work for less.

Thirdly, the economies of Southern Europe are structured in such a way that there are
many temporary and "informal" or "underground" jobs that immigrants will take.
"Informal" and "underground" refer to jobs not reported to government authorities, thus
avoiding regulations and taxes. Southern Europe has many such jobs in tourism, domestic work, agriculture, and construction.

A fourth factor involves colonial and cultural ties between Southern Europe and other
parts of the world. These ties encourage migration streams. One example is the migration
from the Spanish-speaking lands of Central and South America to Spain. Portugal's former African colonies provide another example. Migration to Southern Europe from other
European Union member countries is especially easy. Many of the latter migrants are
professionals and managers or retirees.

Another factor is trade and tourism. Both are important parts of the economies of Southern Europe. These countries encourage visitors and thus are easy to enter. Many migrants come first as tourists.

And lastly, the physical geography of Southern Europe is suited to illegal entry. It has long coastlines, many islands, and mountainous borders.

You Are the Geographer

1. Table 1 displays data on foreign residents in Catalonia (a northeastern region of Spain) in 1970, 1985, and 1995. Similar trends were occurring in many other parts of Southern Europe. Write a paragraph on the changing numbers and origins of migrants.

_____

_____

_____

_____

2. Use the data in Table 2 and the outline map of Spain at the end of this activity to show where foreign residents are concentrated. On a separate sheet of paper, list the autonomous communities (regions) of Spain in rank order from the one with the highest percentage of foreign residents (Ceuta and Melilla) to the one with the lowest (Castilla-La Mancha). Divide the list into four classes. There will be two classes (the highest two) with five autonomous communities each and two with four autonomous communities each. Assign colors to your four classes, using the darkest for the class that has the highest percentages of foreign residents and the lightest for the class that has the lowest percentages. Color each autonomous community correctly.

Now study the pattern on your map. Use the text and other maps in your textbook, atlases, or other sources to help you understand the pattern you see. What is it about the places with higher percentages that make them attractive to immigrants? What is it about the places with lower percentages that make them less attractive?

_____

_____

_____

_____

Name _____ Class _____ Date _____

Table 1.
Foreign resident population by origin, Catalonia, 1970, 1985, 1995

	1970		1985		1995	
	Number	Percentage	Number	Percentage	Number	Percentage
Europe	21,939	68.0	27,219	60.3	36,353	33.4
North America	1,284	4.0	1,672	3.7	2,195	2.0
Central and South America	7,356	22.8	11,308	25.0	23,963	22.0
Asia	902	2.8	2,792	6.2	9,896	9.1
Africa	386	1.2	1,825	4.0	36,408	33.4
Oceania	69	0.2	148	0.3	162	0.1
Others (stateless)	328	1.0	182	0.4	27	0.0
TOTAL	32,264	100.0	45,146	100.0	109,004	100.0

NOTE: Catalonia had about 6 million total residents in 1993.
Source: King, Russell; Gabriella Lazaridis; and Charalambos Tsardanidis, eds. 2000. *Eldorado or Fortress? Migration in Southern Europe.* New York: St. Martins Press, p. 109.

Table 2.
Foreign residents in Spain by autonomous community, 1991

Autonomous Community	Number	Percentage of total population
Andalusia	35,860	0.52
Aragon	3,500	0.29
Asturias	4,630	0.42
Balearic Islands	14,690	2.07
Basque Country	7,720	0.37
Canary Islands	30,280	2.03
Cantabria	1,690	0.32
Castilla-La Mancha	2,370	0.14
Castilla y León	11,670	0.46
Catalonia	56,140	0.93
Ceuta and Melilla	4,140	3.33
Extremadura	2,420	0.23
Galicia	16,040	0.59
La Rioja	680	0.26
Madrid	56,020	1.13
Murcia	3,180	0.30
Navarra	2,560	0.49
Valencia	29,620	0.77
TOTAL	283,210	0.73

NOTE: These figures refer to people counted by the Spanish census. Estimates that include illegal immigrants can be several times as high.
Source: Huntoon, Laura. 1998. Immigration to Spain: Implications for a Unified European Union Immigration Policy. *International Migration Review* 32(2): 431.

Chapter 16, Geography for Life Activities, continued

Spain's Autonomous Communities

Name _____ Class _____ Date _____

National Geography Standard 15   **Waterways of Russia**

Russia's coastline is nearly twice as long as that of the United States (about 23,000 miles versus 12,000 miles). It has about 63,000 miles of navigable inland waterways, more than any other country except China. In this exercise, you will become familiar with Russia's waterways and learn about both their usefulness and their problems.

Begin by using your textbook and an atlas to label the following bodies of water and cities on the map at the end of this activity. Notice as you work how many of Russia's large cities are located on major rivers. The Volga-Kama system is particularly city-rich.

Rivers: Amur, Angara, Don, Irtysh, Kama, Kolyma, Lena, Northern Dvina, Ob', Pechora, Volga, Yenisey

Salt Water Bodies: Sea of Azov, Baltic Sea, Barents Sea, Black Sea, Caspian Sea, East Siberian Sea, Gulf of Finland, Kara Sea, Laptev Sea, Tatar Strait, White Sea

Seaports: Arkangelsk, Astrakhan, Dudinka, Kaliningrad, Murmansk, Novorossiysk, Petropavlovsk Kamchatskiy, Rostov-na-Donau, St. Petersburg, Salekard, Tiksi, Vladivostok

River Ports: Bratsk, Chita, Krasnoyarsk, Moscow, Nizhniy Novgorod, Novosibirsk, Omsk, Samara, Volgograd, Yakutsk

You Are the Geographer

Now that you have completed your map, answer the following questions.

1. Which Russian rivers flow from south to north and empty into seas and bays of the Arctic Ocean?

_____

_____

2. Which river flows from east to west and empties into the Tatar Strait?

_____

3. Which river flows from north to south and empties into the Sea of Azov? Which one flows from north to south and empties into the Caspian Sea? What city is located near the canal that joins these two rivers?

_____

_____

Chapter 17, Geography for Life Activities, continued

4. Which south-flowing river is connected by canals, lakes, and minor rivers northward to the Gulf of Finland and the Baltic?

_____

5. Most Russian seaports are closed by ice part of the year. What are the three exceptions? These three each have some other geographical disability. What is it in each case?

_____

_____

_____

_____

6. Except for Murmansk, all seaports on the Arctic and Pacific sides of Russia are closed by ice in the winter and the spring. In some of these ports, the shipping season is extended by the use of icebreakers. What other ports on other seas are closed part of the year too?

_____

_____

7. Which rivers are ice-bound for half (or longer) of each year? Which river ports are ice-bound for half of each year or longer? Which river ports are ice-bound between one-quarter and one-half of the year?

_____

_____

8. The upper (southern) reaches of Russia's north-flowing rivers melt while the lower (northern) reaches are still frozen. What do you think happens as a result? How does widespread permafrost make this problem worse?

_____

_____

_____

Chapter 17, Geography for Life Activities, continued

9. Railroads are much more important than waterways for moving most kinds of goods in Russia. Use an atlas to identify (a) the part of Russia with the highest density of rail lines and (b) the part of Russia that is completely without rail lines. How may rail lines connect western Russia all the way to the Pacific shore?

_____

_____

_____

_____

10. Russian waterways, in part because of their climatic and locational problems, have not been used nearly as much as they could be. Investment in them has fallen dramatically since the collapse of the Soviet Union. As a result, one-quarter of the system has become dangerously silted up. However, there is a lot of interest from international organizations and European shippers in helping Russia restore and upgrade its waterways in exchange for letting foreign vessels (which are now excluded) use them. What do you think could be the pluses and minuses of such an effort?

_____

_____

_____

_____

_____

Chapter 17, Geography for Life Activities, continued

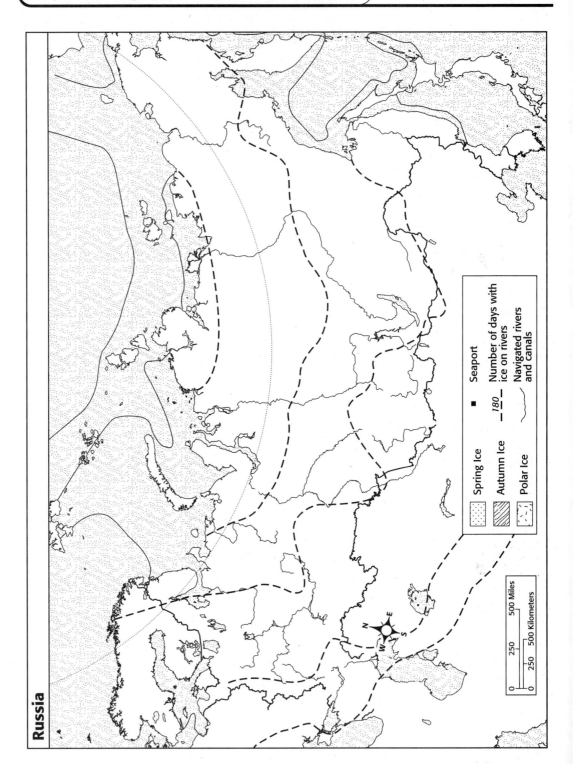

Russia

Legend:
- ■ Seaport
- 180 — Number of days with ice on rivers
- ~~~ Navigated rivers and canals
- Spring Ice
- Autumn Ice
- Polar Ice

500 Miles
250   500 Kilometers
0   250   0

Name _____ Class _____ Date _____

 Geography for Life Activities

National Geography Standard 13   **The Fragmented Fergana Valley**

The Fergana Valley, about 300 kilometers long and 80 kilometers wide, is Central Asia's biggest oasis. It is surrounded by the Tian Shan mountains to the northeast and the Pamir Alay mountains to the southeast. Numerous streams rise in these mountains and flow down to the Fergana Valley where they come together to form the Syr Dar'ya. The Syr Dar'ya flows westward, exiting the valley where it narrows near the city of Khudzhand. In the mountains, the headwaters of the Syr Dar'ya generate hydroelectricity, and in the valley, its waters make possible irrigated agriculture. Today it is a valley torn asunder by conflicting interests.

The Fergana Valley today is shared among three countries: Uzbekistan (which controls about 60 percent of it), Tajikistan (25 percent), and Kyrgyzstan (15 percent). The three Fergana Valley provinces in Uzbekistan (Andijan, Fergana, and Namangan) have 6.2 million people. Parts of Kyrgyzstan's Osh and Jalal-Abad provinces are also in the valley, as is part of Tajikistan's Leninabad province adding 4.2 million people, although some of these live in the surrounding mountains. The valley therefore represents an important concentration of people and economic production for each of the three countries.

Under Soviet Rule

Under the Russians, Kazakhstan became a frontier settlement zone for pioneering Russians and Ukrainians. Much of the rest of Central Asia became a vast irrigated cotton plantation, following Russia's loss of American cotton supplies after the U.S. Civil War. Under the Soviets, the policy of regional economic specialization intensified, and Uzbekistan in particular saw its best lands degraded through the relentless production of cotton. The emphasis on cotton and mineral production, including oil and natural gas, in Central Asia made the region something of an internal colony. Most finished goods were imported by Central Asia from elsewhere in the Soviet Union. When the Soviet Union broke apart in 1989, the five Central Asian republics inherited economies designed as parts of a much larger whole, not ones meant to stand alone.

Another key legacy of the Soviet era is the political geography of Central Asia. The Soviets divided the region up into five republics (Kyrgyzstan, Uzbekistan, Tajikistan, Kazakhstan, and Turkmenistan). This Soviet strategy was in part a means of countering Pan-Islamism and Pan-Turkism. Pan-Islamism refers to efforts to unite all Muslims. Pan-Turkism refers to efforts to unify all Turkish peoples. The Soviets perceived these movements as threats.

The political boundaries drawn by the Soviets are particularly convoluted in the Fergana Valley. They cross and recross rivers, canals, roads, railroads, pipelines, and power lines. When the Central Asian republics were all part of the Soviet Union, the boundaries did not much matter. Now that they are international borders, they are a challenge to efficient spatial interaction and economic development.

Traditional bases of identity in Central Asia were clan, dynasty, religion, and territory. The ideas of national identity and of nation-state were introduced by the Russians. The Russians created not only Uzbekistan, but Uzbeks, not only Kyrgyzstan, but Kyrgyz, and so on. The Russians followed the dictum, "divide and conquer" by encouraging the development of distinctive languages and literatures. They further complicated the future of the region by drawing its political boundaries so that they did not correspond with the distribution of the emerging national groups. Such would have been an impossible task in any case, as the groups lived intermixed. Every country in the region today has sizable minorities whose ethnicity is that of the majority population in neighboring countries.

Under Independent Rule

Economic conditions in the Fergana Valley have become nightmarish since the collapse of the Soviet Union and the independence of the Central Asian nations. Some international aid organizations estimate that the Fergana Valley's rate of unemployment is 80 percent. Many factories and other businesses have closed. Electricity is available for only four hours a day. The farming sector is in trouble, in part because of losses of soil fertility brought about by decades of unsustainable irrigation agriculture. The Soviet-built education and health-care systems are failing. Black markets, organized crime, narcotics production and trade, and the corruption of public officials are major problems. Land, water, and job shortages are worsened by rapid population growth in the region.

Economic strains are intensified by the different paths taken by Kyrgyzstan, Uzbekistan, and Tajikistan since independence. Kyrgyzstan has moved rapidly toward a market economy, while the others have not. The once integrated economy of the Fergana Valley has been further fractured by the emergence of three separate national currencies and by controlled borders.

The severe economic conditions in the Fergana Valley have led to violent conflict. Some of this has taken on an ethnic flavor; for example, the rioting of ethnic Uzbeks and Kyrgyz in Osh, Kyrgyzstan, in 1990 over land, housing, jobs, and political power.

In other cases, the conflict has a religious dimension. Islam is resurgent in Central Asia, following decades of repression by the officially atheist Soviets. Today the Fergana Valley has Central Asia's largest concentration of practicing Muslims. The most well-organized opposition to the existing governments in Central Asia is Islamic. The strongest of these groups, the Islamic Movement of Uzbekistan (IMU), may be turning into a pan-Central Asian cause, and the armies of Uzbekistan, Kyrgyzstan, Tajikistan, and Kazakhstan all are involved in fighting the IMU. In the Fergana Valley, there are also conflicts within Islam. Will local variants of Islam, with their traditions of local pilgrimages, survive in the face of more standardized versions imported from abroad?

One of the most destructive results of the unrest is that it has deepened the suspicion among the three countries that share the Fergana Valley. They accuse one another of plotting with or sheltering their enemies. They withhold resources from one another. For example, in the winter of 2000–2001 Uzbekistan withheld gas supplies from Kyrgyzstan and Tajikistan in part to pressure them to act more aggressively against the IMU.

Chapter 18, Geography for Life Activities, continued

Uzbekistan also land-mined its borders with Kyrgyzstan, separating families and villages and suppressing trade.

You Are the Geographer

The increasing geographical fragmentation of the Fergana Valley only makes solving its critical economic problems more difficult. Using the map on the following page see what additional insights you can gain about this situation by completing the following tasks. Write your answers on a separate piece of paper.

1. Find and circle at least five places on the map of the Fergana Valley where international borders cut across infrastructure (waterways, roads, railroads, pipelines). Also indicate on the map a place where infrastructure has obviously followed a circuitous path to avoid crossing an international border.

2. Use your textbook or an atlas to locate other areas in the world with international boundaries as complex as those of Central Asia. Compare the situation in this other region with the situation in Central Asia.

3. Explain the conflict between an upstream water user such as Kyrgyzstan and downstream water users, such as Uzbekistan and Kazakhstan. Remember to consider the various uses of water.

4. Use the Internet to find the most up-to-date news you can on Central Asia (and the Fergana Valley if possible). How has the region's complex geography shaped the current events you identified?

5. How could the Central Asian governments and the rest of the world help overcome the fragmentation of the region? Brainstorm ideas with your class or a small group. Some steps may be geographical, others not.

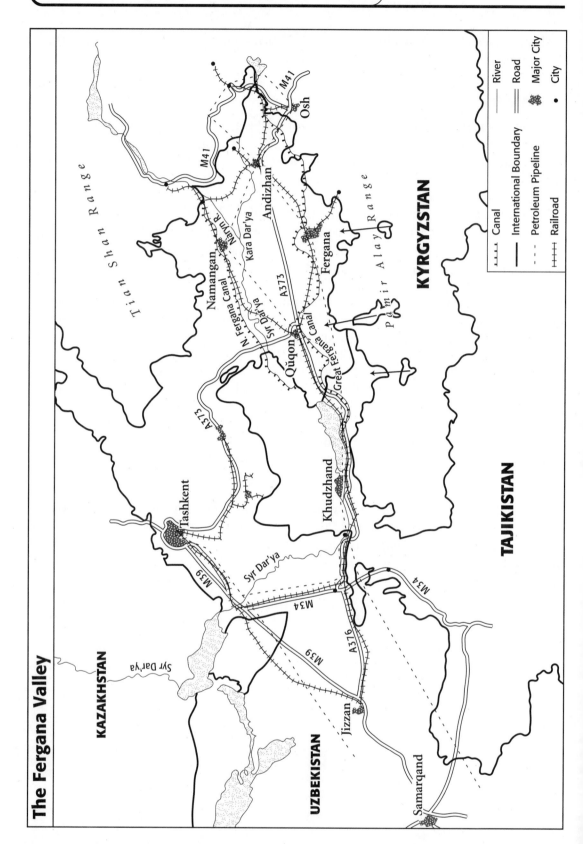

The Fergana Valley

Name _____ Class _____ Date _____

Geography for Life Activities

National Geography Standard 1

Speaking Graphically about Persian Gulf Oil

In this exercise you will examine and graphically display information about Persian Gulf oil. The term "Persian Gulf," when used in government statistics on oil production, applies to the following countries: Bahrain, Iran, Iraq, Kuwait, Qatar, Saudi Arabia, and the United Arab Emirates (U.A.E.). In this exercise, we will add to that group Oman (on the Gulf of Oman and the Arabian Sea) and Yemen (on the Gulf of Aden).

In 2000 the seven Persian Gulf countries produced 28 percent of the world's oil, while possessing 65 percent of the world's oil reserves. Oil imported from the Persian Gulf region met 13 percent of U.S. demand, 22 percent of Western Europe's demand, and 73 percent of Japan's demand. In addition to oil, the Persian Gulf has one third of the world's proven reserves of natural gas.

Ninety percent of the petroleum that is exported from the Persian Gulf goes by tanker through the Strait of Hormuz between Iran and Oman. The significance of the energy resource, together with the choke point through which it must pass, makes the Persian Gulf of immense strategic importance to a hydrocarbon-dependent world. Military spending as a share of national income is higher in this region than almost anywhere else in the world. When it comes, a world shift toward alternative forms of energy will have a big effect on the economy and politics of the region.

You Are the Geographer

Use an atlas or your textbook to correctly fill in these nine country names, plus the Persian, Arabian, and Red Seas and the Gulfs of Oman and Aden on the outline map provided at the end of this activity. You are most likely familiar with a map of the Persian Gulf region that looks like the outline map included in this exercise. The sizes of countries on that map are in the same proportion to one another as their sizes on Earth. The actual Saudi Arabia is five times as large as the actual Iraq, and the same relationship exists on the map. Suppose that instead we want a map of the Persian Gulf region on which the sizes of the countries are in proportion to the size of their crude oil reserves. Saudi Arabia has oil reserves that are 2.3 times as large as those of Iraq, so on this map, the ratio between their sizes will be 2.3: 1, not 5:1. We also want to maintain to the extent possible the spatial arrangement of the countries involved. Such a map is called a cartogram.

Construct a Cartogram To construct the cartogram, you will need a sheet of graph paper, a pencil, the outline map of the Persian Gulf, and data from either column 3 or column 4 of Table 1. (Half of your class could map the column 3 data, and half the column 4 data.) First decide how many barrels of oil one small square (.25 inch) on your graph paper will represent. In the case of crude oil reserves (column 3), one square might equal one billion barrels; in the case of crude oil production (column 4), one square might equal one million barrels. Having determined your scale, figure out how many

(73)

Geography for Life Activities

Chapter 19, Geography for Life Activities, *continued*

squares each country should occupy. If you use the scale of one square equals one billion barrels (in column 3), then on your graph paper Bahrain will occupy one tenth of a square, Iran will occupy 89.7 squares, Iraq 112.5, and so on. The next step is to figure out what shape each country should have and how to place them relative to each other, so that their arrangement is as much as possible like it is in the real world. Refer to the outline map as you do this. For this exercise, stick to using whole squares and working in large blocks of squares; spatial arrangement is more important than country shape. Be sure and have a Persian Gulf on your cartogram, as well as the nine countries. You will probably find yourself erasing a lot, as you try to get the nine countries, now having new proportions, into their familiar spatial pattern. When you are satisfied, label the countries and give your cartogram a title and a scale. If you were to do this for the entire world, Saudi Arabia and the United States would be about the same size on a map of current production, but Saudi Arabia would be ten times the size of the United States on a map of reserves.

Construct a Graph The cartogram you made is concerned with one variable, oil reserves or oil production. The second type of graphic you will produce displays the relationship between two variables, oil production per capita and Gross National Income (GNI) per capita. It will help you examine the proposition that those countries producing lots of oil per capita also have high per capita incomes. You will need another sheet of graph paper for this part of the exercise.

Begin by calculating crude oil production per capita. To do this divide the figures in column 4 by those in column 5, and create a new column in which to put the answers. For example, for Bahrain, divide 47,000 by 700,000; for an answer of .07. This means that every day in 1999, Bahrain produced .07 barrel of oil per each Bahrain resident. Do the same calculation for each country listed.

Make a graph, using graph paper. On the horizontal axis will be oil production per capita and on the vertical axis will be Gross National Income (GNI) per capita. Figure out reasonable scales for these axes and put them on your paper. Then graph the 9 points. "Eyeball" a straight line through the points. This line is a graphic expression of the relationship between the two variables. From it you can approximate how much income per capita goes up as oil production per capita goes up.

Which points fall farthest from your line? Those countries whose points fall above the line have higher incomes than predicted, given their oil production, while those below the line have lower incomes than predicted, given their oil production. This has to do with the fact that, dependent as they are on oil, Persian Gulf states have other dimensions to their economies too. The small states, which have been extremely dependent on oil income for the last few decades, have been trying to diversify their economies into the manufacturing and service sectors. How these other enterprises are going will affect GNI. It is important to remember too, that the figures for GNI per capita are averages. These figures say nothing about income distribution within a country; that is, about how the country's income is shared among people of different classes.

A Third Way to Present Data This exercise in the graphic presentation of data can be extended by trying a third method of mapping, using the outline map provided as your

Name _____ Class _____ Date _____

base map. Use the figures on GNI per capita or other counted data you find on your own. Choose a symbol and make the height or area of the symbol proportional to the value for each country. Place the symbols on the countries and give your map a title and a legend.

More ambitious is to display percentage data in a pie chart for each country and then place each pie chart where it belongs on your map. For example, many countries in the Persian Gulf region have large numbers of foreign residents who have migrated there for work. A pie chart for each country could show what percent of the population is indigenous and what percent is foreign. You might even be able to find what share of each country's population comes from various world regions. These would be represented as appropriately sized slices of each country's population pie.

Be sure to include on your map the date of your data, as your map is much less useful without this piece of information. For example, before the Gulf War many of Kuwait's migrant workers were Palestinians; after the war the Kuwaitis excluded many Palestinians in favor of South Asians who were perceived as less likely to raise political issues. If you mapped this kind of information, your map reader would want to know if the picture being presented was prewar or postwar.

Write two paragraphs. In the first one summarize what you learned about the Persian Gulf region. In the second give examples of other projects or topics where the graphic methods you practiced in this exercise might be useful.

Table 1. Persian Gulf Region (including Oman and Yemen), Selected Statistics

Country	Area	Crude Oil Reserves 2000	Crude Oil Production 1999	Population (Millions), 2000	GNI per capita 1999
Bahrain	266	0.1	47	0.7	$13,700
Iran	630,575	89.7	3,632	66.1	$5,300
Iraq	169,236	112.5	2,523	23.6	$2,700
Kuwait	6,880	96.5	2,013	2.3	$22,500
Oman	82,031	5.3	893	2.4	$8,000
Qatar	4,247	3.7	776	0.6	$17,000
Saudi Arabia	829,996	263.5	8,499	21.1	$9,000
U.A.E.	32,278	97.8	2,329	3.3	$17,700
Yemen	203,849	4.0	409	18.0	$750
TOTAL	1,959,358	673.1	21,121	138.1	$5,550
United States	3,717,796	21.8	8,107	284.5	$33,900
World	57,900,000	1,016.8	72,663	6,137.0	$6,800

NOTE: Area is expressed in square miles. Oil reserves are expressed in billion barrels. Crude oil production is expressed as 1000 barrels per day. GNI=Gross National Income.
Sources: C. I. A.; Population Reference Bureau; U.S. Energy Information Administration.

Name _____ Class _____ Date _____

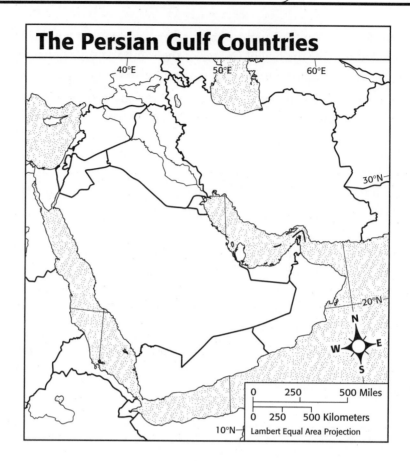

The Persian Gulf Countries

Geography for Life Activities

National Geography Standard 17   **Site and Situation Shape Byzantium/Constantinople/Istanbul**

Why are cities located in some places and not others? Why do cities in some places become great, while others remain small? Geographers who seek to answer these questions often begin by distinguishing between site and situation.

Site refers to the features of the terrain on which a settlement began and over which it has spread. Relief, geology, soils, flora and fauna, water supply and water bodies (rivers, lakes, harbors), local natural hazards (flooding, earthquakes), and microclimate (for example, susceptibility to local fogs or high winds) are all features of site.

Situation refers to the larger setting of a city. It includes the same kinds of physical features mentioned above, only on a regional scale. For example, whether a patch of ground is sufficiently drained to support buildings is a site issue; whether regional soils are productive enough to grow adequate food for a city's population is a situation issue. The most important aspect of situation is location relative to a natural transportation route such as a coast, a river, or a path through a mountain pass. A nodal situation, in which a city is a node where multiple transportation routes meet, is the most advantageous of all situations.

The distinction between site and situation is illustrated by the following example. A coast is an advantageous situation, assuming that boats or ships are available to link one settlement with another. A good natural harbor along that same coast provides an advantageous site. In general, an advantageous situation is more important than an advantageous site, in part because sites are easier to modify.

People transform both sites and situations. They change a city's site as they deepen harbors, build levees, drain marshes, flatten hilltops, remove trees. They change a city's situation by building new transportation links (roads, railroads, airports), exhausting old resources and discovering new ones, and rearranging political boundaries that alter patterns of interaction. Over time, a city's site and situation are defined not just by natural endowment, but also by how they have been shaped by people.

The Ideal Situation

Istanbul (formerly Byzantium and Constantinople) has one of the world's most attractive situations. Its desirability is suggested by the fact that no other city in the world has suffered as many attacks or sieges. Istanbul has endured onslaughts by Persians, Athenians, Macedonians, Gauls, Romans, Goths, Slavs, Avars, Arabs, Bulgarians, Russians, Pechenegs, Crusaders, Byzantines, and Ottomans. Other groups, including the British and the French, have helped defend the city in order to keep it from falling into the hands of their enemies. Many people have believed that this is a place worth fighting for!

One look at a map will help explain why. Istanbul is located on the Bosporus, the narrow strait between Europe and Asia that connects the Sea of Marmara with the Black Sea. Used since ancient times for travel and trade, this water route links the Aegean and

Mediterranean seas with the Black Sea. Political geographers call such a strategic narrows a *choke point.* Whoever commands a choke point wields influence over others who wish to pass through it. Powers based along the Black Sea, notably the Russians, have made many efforts to capture Istanbul and gain control of the Bosporus.

Crossing the Bosporus at Istanbul is also one of the world's great land routes, connecting the Balkans and central Europe with Southwest Asia and the Persian Gulf. Here was one of the places where the products of the east met the products of the west. Some were consumed in the great city that was Constantinople. Others continued on their journeys, some having made a switch in transport mode from land to water or vice versa or from one type of vessel or pack animal to another. Places where goods have to be unloaded and repacked are called *break-of-bulk points,* and cities often grow up at such points.

Greek and Roman Rule

The exact site of Istanbul is credited to the presence of the Golden Horn. This is a 5-mile-long northern inlet of the Bosporus. It provides a harbor so deep and sheltered that for centuries even the largest boats could unload directly to the shore using wooden planks. This superb natural harbor was one of the reasons the site was selected by Greek colonists about 660 B.C. Three sides of the old city are surrounded by water, the Golden Horn to the north, the Bosporus to the east, and the Sea of Marmara to the south. From the 400s A.D., the city was protected by some of the most impressive walls in Europe, and an artificial moat along the western side completed its watery defenses.

Byzantium was a valuable port in the Roman Empire. Even so, it was razed in 196 B.C. by the Roman emperor, as it had sided against him in a civil war. It was soon rebuilt. In 324 A.D., Constantine reunified the Roman Empire after a period of division and growing chaos in the western reaches of the empire. Byzantium became its new capital city, which was renamed Constantinople and dedicated to the Virgin Mary. The emperor referred to it as New Rome, and indeed the site had seven hills, just like the site of Rome.

Also like Rome, Constantinople became one of the world's great imperial cities, serving as the capital of the Byzantine (eastern Roman) Empire for more than a millennium. For centuries, it was Europe's most important commercial city. It was also an ecclesiastical center. The patriarch of Constantinople was second only to the bishop of Rome among Christian leaders, and when eastern and western Christianity split in the 1000s, the patriarch became the head of the eastern (Orthodox) church. Constantinople's crossroads location facilitated these administrative, commercial, and religious roles. It also contributed to its becoming a city of many different ethnicities, languages, and religions. Such a city is said to be *cosmopolitan,* meaning a city of the world.

The Byzantine Empire gradually lost territory to the Arabs and Turks (peoples newly inspired by the fervor of Islam), and to rising powers on the Italian peninsula. Constantinople was pillaged for years following its capture by Crusaders in 1204. The city decayed and lost population until it was finally overcome by the Ottoman Turks in 1453. Using cannon, they breached the ancient walls for the first and only time in the city's history.

Ottoman Rule

Constantinople became the capital of the Ottoman Empire four years later. By the mid-1500s the empire reached from Algeria to the Caspian Sea and Persian Gulf and from Hungary and Transylvania to Yemen. It included much of the same territory as had the Byzantine Empire. And like Byzantium before it, Constantinople welcomed people from all parts of its empire and beyond. It was the multinational capital of a multinational empire, including Turks, Greeks, Franks, Kurds, Serbs, Arabs and others. In 1477, 59 percent of the population was Muslim, 23 percent Orthodox Christian, 5 percent Armenian Christian, 9 percent Jewish, and 4 percent "other." The share that was Muslim did not go above 59 percent until after 1920 when the empire was gone and the capital of the modern state of Turkey was moved to Ankara.

Under the Ottomans, Constantinople continued not only its function as imperial capital, but also its earlier established role as religious headquarters. The city became the capital of Islam in the sense that the Ottoman sultan was the most powerful Muslim ruler, the supreme Imam (leader of prayer), and the guardian of the pilgrimage routes to the two holy cities of Medina and Mecca. By the 1700s the Ottoman government was spending 10 to 17 percent of its total revenue on protecting the pilgrimage routes, providing inns, armed escorts, and bribes to pacify Bedouin tribes along the way. Constantinople also remained the seat of the Patriarch of the Orthodox Church, whose power extended into areas not part of the Ottoman Empire, including Russia. The councils of the Orthodox Church were held in Constantinople. Orthodox pilgrims traveled to Constantinople to visit shrines and relics, and then continued on to Jerusalem.

Constantinople thrived as a commercial center under Ottoman rule. It was the largest city and one of the largest ports in the Mediterranean. The scale of activity in the port, with hundreds of large ships and 15,000 small boats, often stunned newcomers to the city. The Ottomans favored trade, and established diplomatic relations with rival countries or, conversely, went to war with them over trade routes. France became the empire's main Western trading partner. Constantinople imported cloth, paper, leather, and glass from France, and returned raw wool, hides, silk, and luxury goods, including caviar and processed goat's hair (for wigs). Trade was the basis of the city's prosperity, and with it came population growth, from 80,000 to 400,000 in the period 1477–1530. In 1600 and 1700 Constantinople was the largest city in Europe, and it was surpassed by only London and Paris in 1800. The city's dependence on trade helped it welcome Jews far longer than had Christian nations to the west; Armenians were also an important component of the merchant class. Thus the city's excellent situation for trade may be seen as a factor in shaping its ethnic character.

The Decline of the Ottoman Empire

The Ottoman Empire was under increasing stress in the 1800s. The forces of industrialization that were changing the economies of Western Europe were weak. Railroads and factories did not alter the site and situation of Constantinople like they did so many other European cities. Planned improvements to the port—so essential a facility in the economy of Constantinople—were postponed. Electricity came late to most of the city.

While a bridge of local significance (over the Golden Horn) was opened in 1845, no bridge over the Bosporus was built until 1973, even though metropolitan Istanbul had long since leaped the strait and could have used a bridge much earlier, as could have long-distance travel.

After World War I, the Ottoman Empire was dismembered and the modern country of Turkey was created. The leader of the new Turkey, Kemal Atatürk, was determined to use nationalism as a basis for unifying the new state. He worked to shape a modern Turkish identity and distanced the new government from the multiculturalism of the old Ottoman Empire. He also wanted removal from what he perceived as the weaknesses of the old order, including corruption and the power of religious figures. Furthermore, Istanbul (as it was now called) was not so centrally located in Turkey as it had been in its former empire. So the city of one million that had been an imperial capital for 1,593 years became the second city of Turkey, and Ankara, a crude country town of 20,000, became the new national capital.

Today, 75 years later, Ankara has grown to 2.5 million people, an indication of what resources a national capital can command. Istanbul has about 8 million people and remains Turkey's number one city in commerce, manufacturing, education, and the arts.

You Are the Geographer

Now choose another city in the Eastern Mediterranean (listed below) and find out about its site and situation. How have these helped or hindered the growth of the city? How have the city's site and situation changed through time? Write a few paragraphs summarizing your ideas. Illustrate your essay with sketch maps of your city's site and situation. Essential sources include maps, encyclopedias, guidebooks, and historical atlases, such as *The Times Atlas of World History. Webster's Geographical Dictionary* provides useful leads. Books on the histories of particular cities can be very helpful.

Turkey:	Ankara, Izmir (ancient Smyrna), Trabazon/Trebizond (ancient Trapezeus
Syria:	Aleppa (ancient Beroea), Damascus, Homs/Hims (ancient Emesa, Latakia/Al Ladhiqiyah (ancient Laodicea)
Lebanon:	Beirut (ancient Berytus), Sidon/Sayda, Tyre/Sur (ancient Tyrus)
Israel:	Acra/Akko, Gaza, Haifa (ancient Sycaminum), Jersualem, Tel Aviv-Jaffa/Tel Aviv-Yafo
Jordan:	Amman (ancient Philadelphia)
Cyprus:	Nicosia

Name _____ Class _____ Date _____

In arid lands, water is the most precious resource. Its spatial distribution helps to determine patterns of human settlement and land use. One of the most important uses of water in dry environments is irrigated agriculture. In this exercise you will learn about the history and geography of irrigated agriculture in the countries of North Africa. A recent water development project in Libya, the Great Man-Made River, will be highlighted.

In ancient times, the Mediterranean region produced legumes, fodder crops, millet, fruit trees, and vegetables using irrigation. The largest cities were surrounded by truck gardens, just as they are now. In the driest southern and eastern margins, nearly all agriculture depended on some irrigation. In North Africa, it was used along the Nile in Egypt, around the towns of Cyrenaica (eastern Libya), and in many locations, both coastal and interior, in the Atlas Mountains. Sources of water included surface streams, springs, and aquifers.

In post-classical times, a Southwest Asian technology for tapping ground water, known as *qanats* in Iraq, diffused to North Africa. These are systems of underground conduits that use gravity flow to collect ground water and channel it to surface canals for distribution to fields. In some locations, these systems still function. However, in many places more modern, but less sustainable, irrigation technologies have replaced them. The Arabs also brought new crops that required irrigation, including rice and citrus.

Managing Water Supplies

Ensuring adequate water supplies for growing populations is a major concern of North African countries. Algeria and Tunisia are already considered to be suffering from water stress. This means they have less than an annual minimum of 1000 cubic meters of water per capita, an amount judged necessary to maintain public health and support development. Water stress is predicted for Morocco, Libya, and Egypt by 2050.

In Libya, the demand for water more than doubled between 1977 and 1994. During that same period, the population nearly doubled (from 2.72 to 5.24 million), and the output of many agricultural products increased severalfold. Much of the water in Libya is fossil ground water. It is a legacy from tens of thousands of years ago when the Sahara had a wetter climate. It is a nonrenewable resource. The Libyan government hopes the water will last for 50 years.

The water from the two southerly regions of Libya is being delivered to the populous and intensively farmed north by means of the Great Man-Made River. When complete, this $25-billion-dollar project will be the biggest underground pipeline network on Earth. Portions of the 13-foot-diameter pipeline that are complete run from the vicinity of Tāzirbū to Benghazi, with a branch connecting Ajdābiyah to Surt, and from the vicinity of Birak to Tripoli and Misrātah. Tripoli and Misrātah are also connected. A section linking Misrātah with Surt is under construction. Several additional pipelines are planned.

Part of the water being delivered by the Great Man-Made River is replacing water pumped from aquifers near the coast where falling water tables have caused serious salt-water intrusion and soil salinization. The rest of the water is permitting the expansion of irrigated agriculture and greater self-sufficiency in food, an important government priority.

You Are the Geographer

To see the scale of irrigation in North Africa today, study and complete Table 1 on the following page. Answer the following questions on a separate piece of paper.

1. Which North African country has the largest absolute area of irrigated agriculture in the region and also the largest share of its agricultural land irrigated?

2. Which North African country has about the same percentage of its agricultural land irrigated as Mexico, although a much smaller absolute amount?

3. Which country has only about 6 percent as much irrigated land as the United States, but about the same share of agricultural land irrigated?

4. Taken together, the five countries of North Africa have about the same absolute amount of irrigated land as which North American country? Taken together, the five countries of North Africa have about the same share of their agricultural land irrigated as which North American country?

5. How does North Africa's percentage of agricultural land irrigated compare to the same figure for Africa as a whole and to the world as a whole?

6. Outside of North Africa, African countries with sizable areas of irrigated agriculture are Madagascar, South Africa, and Sudan. What is a reason other than climate for the greater presence of irrigation in some places?

7. Table 2 on the following page shows the water recharge and use in five regions in Libya. About 95 percent of available water in Libya is ground water. Complete the table by subtracting the 1994 use figures from the recharge figures. The result will be the positive or negative water balance for each region. What did you discover?

8. On the map at the end of this activity, draw the portions of the pipeline that run from Tāzirbū to Benghazi, with a branch connecting Ajdābiyah to Surt, and from the vicinity of Birak to Tripoli and Misrātah, with the latter two places also connected. The Great Man-Made River Project took many years to plan. Why did project planners decide to bring the water to the north, rather than bring agriculture and people to the south?

Name _____ Class _____ Date _____

9. Libya's fossil ground water is clean and abundant, but it is being used up. The Libyans are going to have to take other actions to secure adequate water supplies in the future. What might these be?

Table 1.
Land Use in North Africa and North America, 1997 (1,000s of hectares)

	Arable Land and Land under Permanent Crops	Irrigated Land	Percent of Arable Land Irrigated
World	1,510,442	267,727	_____
Africa	199,340	12,314	_____
Algeria	8,040	560	_____
Egypt	3,300	3300	_____
Libya	2,115	470	_____
Morocco	9,595	1,251	_____
Tunisia	4,900	380	_____
Canada	45,700	720	_____
Mexico	27,300	6,500	_____
United States	179,000	21,400	_____

Source: FAO Production Yearbook 1998.

Table 2.
Water Recharge and Use in Libya (millions of cubic meters per year)

Region	Recharge	Water Use 1977	Water Use 1994	Water Balance
Jifarah Plain and Jabal Nafūsah	300	864	1,750	_____
The Middle Region	150	178	400	_____
Aljabal Alkhdar	340	225	400	_____
Fezzan	0	315	500	_____
Al-Kufrah and Assarir	0	214	1,500	_____

Source: El Asswad, Rabaj M. 1995 "Agricultural Prospects and Water Resources in Libya." *Ambia* 24(6): 324–327.

Libya's Man-Made River

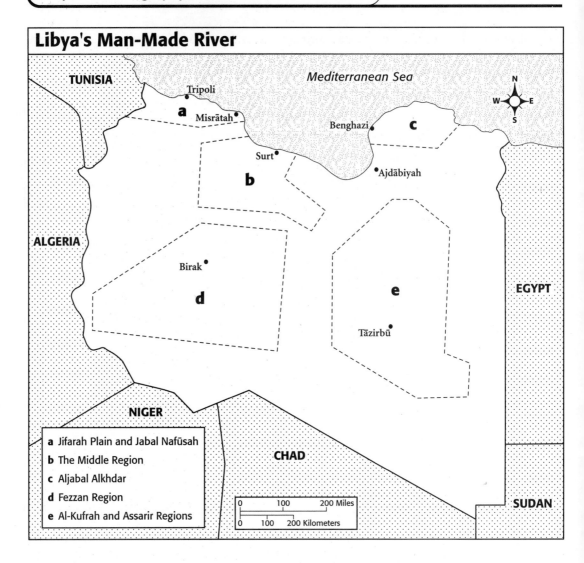

TUNISIA

Mediterranean Sea

Tripoli

a

Misrātah

Benghazi

c

Surt

Ajdābiyah

b

ALGERIA

Birak

d

EGYPT

e

Tāzirbū

NIGER

a Jifarah Plain and Jabal Nafūsah
b The Middle Region
c Aljabal Alkhdar
d Fezzan Region
e Al-Kufrah and Assarir Regions

CHAD

SUDAN

0   100   200 Miles
0   100   200 Kilometers

Name _____ Class _____ Date _____

Geography for Life Activities

National Geography Standard 11

Nigeria's Changing Air Transport Network

As countries shift away from subsistence production toward more commerce, their transportation and communications networks become denser. More and more places are connected by more and more links. The speed of travel along the links also becomes greater. Spatial interaction increases. We can observe this process in the case of the Nigerian domestic air transport network.

Nigeria, with 123 million people, is the most populous country in Africa and the tenth most populous country in the world. Territorially, Nigeria is about the size of Texas, Louisiana, and Arkansas combined. The southern part of the country, facing the Gulf of Guinea, has a humid tropical rain forest climate. As you travel northward, you encounter first a seasonally dry tropical savanna region, and then in the country's far north, a dry steppe climate. In addition to diverse natural environments, Nigeria has a diverse population comprised of some 250 ethnic and linguistic groups. The largest groups are the Yoruba in the southwest, the Ibo in the southeast, and the Hausa and the Fulani in the north. About 50 percent of Nigerians are Muslims, who are concentrated in the north, 40 percent are Christians, who are concentrated in the south, and 10 percent are animists.

Early Transportation Networks

Beginning in the 1800s, the British gradually extended their power over the territory that is modern-day Nigeria. The British extracted cash crops from Nigeria, including palm products, cocoa, rubber, and timber from the south and cotton and peanuts from the north. To facilitate their administration and economic exploitation of Nigeria, the British developed a transport system, including ports, railroads, and roads.

Geographers who have studied the colonial transport systems of Nigeria and of other colonies note that they were designed primarily to connect interior producing regions with coastal ports. From these colonial ports, raw materials flowed to the great ports of Europe, and manufactured goods returned. There was little effort to build transportation linkages for trade internal to a single colony or among colonies. For example, no railroad linking the colonies of West Africa was ever built by the British or French. Check in an atlas and you will see that even today, no such basic piece of infrastructure exists to tie together the West African nations. Think of the contrast between this situation and the dense railroad network that connects the countries of Western Europe.

Figure 1 at the end of this activity illustrates the three types of networks for transportation. "A" is a branching network. It has the shortest total interpoint connections and the lowest construction costs. Connections between some nearby points are poor. This is characteristic of developing country transportation systems. "B" is a circuit network, having the shortest connections between points. It has lower user costs, but higher construction costs than "A," and is characteristic of a developed country. "C" is a hierarchy network, which is the shortest set of connections between a central point and all other points. This is characteristic of transportation systems in a country or region with a primate city (a single especially large and dominant place). Hub-and-spoke systems, such as those used by many American airlines today, are hierarchy networks.

You Are the Geographer

To see how Nigeria changed as the country's economy evolved, do the following:

1. Use the map on the next page and the data below it to show the transportation network in 1930, 1950, 1975, and 1984. Use a different color to show the links that were added in each period. Provide a key for your map.

2. Use the second map (the one which has Nigeria's railroad system on it) and the data provided below it to show the air transport network in the 1990s.

3. Write a paragraph or two comparing the network at each stage with the three types of transportation networks.

4. Find out what happened economically and politically to Nigeria in the 1970s and the 1980s to explain the tremendous changes in the domestic airline network between 1975 and 1984 and between 1984 and the 1990s. (Like the network, the number of passengers expanded tremendously in the earlier period and then fell by one-third in the later one.) An almanac or encyclopedia will have the information you need.

   The airlines operating in Nigeria were not only subject to the general economic and political trends sweeping the country. Beginning in 1988, the Nigerian government began to deregulate and privatize its airline industry, in response to many complaints about the poor service provided by the monopolistic government-owned Nigeria Airways. While at first the government required that private operators continue to serve money-losing routes, later this requirement was relaxed.

   Now write a paragraph that explains what was behind the dramatic changes in Nigeria's domestic passenger air network from the 1970s to the 1990s.

5. Lagos is Nigeria's primate city. Ibadan is the second largest in the country, followed by Kano. How do you explain the different fates of Ibadan and Kano with respect to air service in the 1990s?

Types of Transportation Networks

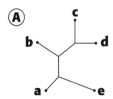 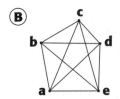 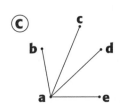

Name _____ Class _____ Date _____

Nigeria's Domestic Air Transport Linkages, 1930–1984

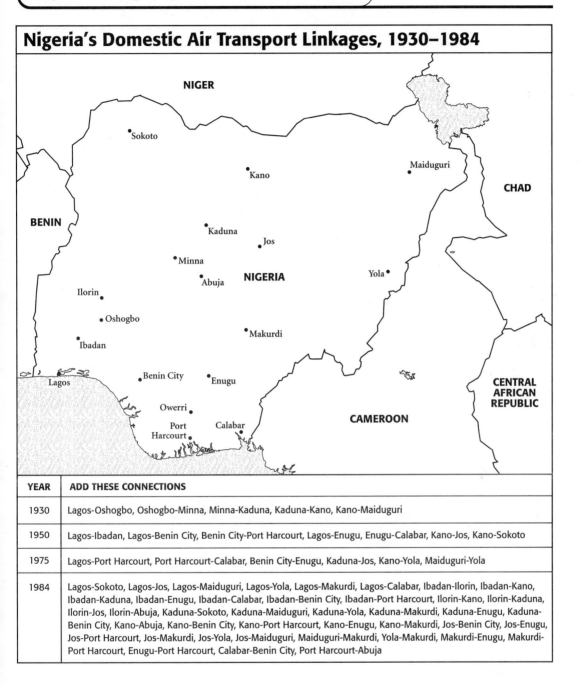

YEAR	ADD THESE CONNECTIONS
1930	Lagos-Oshogbo, Oshogbo-Minna, Minna-Kaduna, Kaduna-Kano, Kano-Maiduguri
1950	Lagos-Ibadan, Lagos-Benin City, Benin City-Port Harcourt, Lagos-Enugu, Enugu-Calabar, Kano-Jos, Kano-Sokoto
1975	Lagos-Port Harcourt, Port Harcourt-Calabar, Benin City-Enugu, Kaduna-Jos, Kano-Yola, Maiduguri-Yola
1984	Lagos-Sokoto, Lagos-Jos, Lagos-Maiduguri, Lagos-Yola, Lagos-Makurdi, Lagos-Calabar, Ibadan-Ilorin, Ibadan-Kano, Ibadan-Kaduna, Ibadan-Enugu, Ibadan-Calabar, Ibadan-Benin City, Ibadan-Port Harcourt, Ilorin-Kano, Ilorin-Kaduna, Ilorin-Jos, Ilorin-Abuja, Kaduna-Sokoto, Kaduna-Maiduguri, Kaduna-Yola, Kaduna-Makurdi, Kaduna-Enugu, Kaduna-Benin City, Kano-Abuja, Kano-Benin City, Kano-Port Harcourt, Kano-Enugu, Kano-Makurdi, Jos-Benin City, Jos-Enugu, Jos-Port Harcourt, Jos-Makurdi, Jos-Yola, Jos-Maiduguri, Maiduguri-Makurdi, Yola-Makurdi, Makurdi-Enugu, Makurdi-Port Harcourt, Enugu-Port Harcourt, Calabar-Benin City, Port Harcourt-Abuja

Name _____ Class _____ Date _____

Nigeria's Domestic Air Transport Linkages, 1990

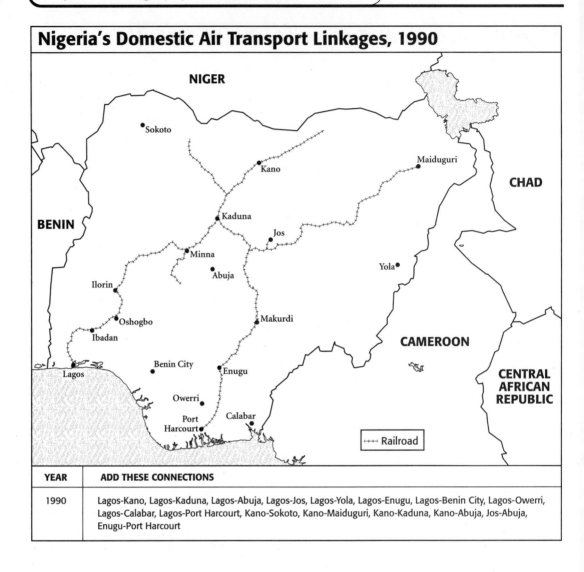

YEAR	ADD THESE CONNECTIONS
1990	Lagos-Kano, Lagos-Kaduna, Lagos-Abuja, Lagos-Jos, Lagos-Yola, Lagos-Enugu, Lagos-Benin City, Lagos-Owerri, Lagos-Calabar, Lagos-Port Harcourt, Kano-Sokoto, Kano-Maiduguri, Kano-Kaduna, Kano-Abuja, Jos-Abuja, Enugu-Port Harcourt

(ACTIVITY **23**)   Geography for Life Activities

National Geography Standard 6   **Struggles Over Africa's
                                         National Parks**

*Geographers are interested in the physical and cultural features of places. They
are also interested in how people perceive and interpret places. Sometimes this
subject of study is called environmental perception. Geographers and other
scholars know that different individuals and groups can have very different perceptions of the same place. This exercise illustrates the different ways that conservationists and local farmers and herders view Africa's national parks. You
will then create a piece of work that communicates these clashing visions.*

In examining the issue of environmental perception, we will use the work of geographer
Roderick P. Neumann. His 1998 book, *Imposing Wilderness: Struggles over Livelihood and
Nature Preservation in Africa,* presents a case study of Arusha National Park in highland
Tanzania. This park consists of 13,700 hectares of land that lie between 1,525 and 4,565
meters in elevation. It contains three distinct habitats: the swampy floor of Ngurdoto
Crater, the rugged volcanic slopes of Mount Meru (the third highest peak in Africa), and
the seven Momela lakes, formed by subsidiary craters and the blocking of drainage lines
by their eruptions. Most of the park is covered with forest or thicket, which is home to
such animals as the elephant, buffalo, hippo, giraffe, eland, colobus monkeys, and numerous bird species.

   Tanzania is among the worlds leading countries in terms of share of its national territory given some kind of protection—27.8 percent, according to the World Conservation
Monitoring Center. Only one country in Africa (Zambia) and eight countries worldwide
have protected a larger percentage of their land. The figure for the United States is 20.3
percent. Tanzania's effort is rather remarkable considering that is generally ranked among
the ten poorest countries in the world, with many people directly dependent on the land
and its resources for their livelihood.

Protecting Nature or the Myth of Nature?

The concept of national parks and other nature preserves developed out of a Euro-
American nature aesthetic. Nature aesthetic means an appreciation of nature largely
based on its beauty and the pleasure it gives the senses. For most of their history
Europeans perceived nature as something frightening and unruly that needed taming and
improving. But as wilderness shrank under the impact of the Industrial Revolution, it
became rare and precious, and the European upper classes developed an appreciation for
it. Landscape painting helped Europeans see nature as pretty scenery. Pristine landscapes
were no longer hideous; they were now beautiful and sublime. They provided first the
upper classes and later the middle classes with important leisure opportunities. By the
1800s, being able to appreciate the beauty and majesty of nature indicated that you were
educated and refined in your tastes.

Chapter 23, Geography for Life Activities, *continued*

An important myth or story for European colonists in many parts of the world was the myth of wilderness conquest. European colonial identities revolved around how Europeans had come from the most advanced part of the world to a much more primitive one and had successfully settled and civilized it. Preserving parts of it in its natural state alongside the developed parts would show just what had been accomplished. Protected areas would also provide opportunities for leisure, including big game hunting, an important pastime for some wealthy white men.

The trouble with this picture was that the places that Europeans appropriated as nature reserves and national parks were not untouched by humans. Often they had been occupied and used by indigenous peoples for hundreds of years. These peoples had profound spiritual attachments to these lands, as well as relying on them for sustenance. But by framing the preserves and parks as natural landscapes, it was easier for the European settlers to deny the claims of indigenous peoples to them.

Arusha National Park and the Meru

The largest ethnic group in what would become the Arusha National Park in Tanzania was the Meru. Their emergence as a relatively coherent social group occurred with their arrival on Mount Meru perhaps 200 years before the arrival of the first Europeans in the late 1800s. Their economy took advantage of the varied ecological zones in the region. Diverse crops, including bananas, maize, sweet potatoes, beans, and millet, were cultivated on individually held plots of land. Cattle herding was also important. The forest provided honey, building materials, fuel wood, and medicines. There was some hunting of wild animals.

German settlers, who engaged in coffee growing, cattle raising, and dairying took the best Meru agricultural land. The mountain slopes above 1,617 meters were designated as forest and game reserves. While the Meru continued to farm the land remaining to them, the loss of customary watering locations and routes of movement seriously impaired herd management. After World War I, the British took over the colony from the Germans, and subsequently more land went to white settlers. As more Meru were forced to share less land, tensions within families and clans mounted, as did those between the Meru and colonial authorities. The Meru developed various means of resisting British directives, such as squatting and trespassing.

Before the colonization of Mount Meru and the surrounding region by Europeans, the indigenous peoples had developed a system whereby they shared the forest and game resources on commonly held lands. When the Germans and later the British set up forest and game reserves, these ancient rights were called into question. Over many decades the rights of indigenous peoples to gather forest products, to hunt, to graze their animals, and to use established rights-of-way were whittled away. Many colonial administrators before World War II were fairly sympathetic to the Meru's exercising of their traditional rights. After the war, resource professionals began taking over. They were less likely to tolerate the Meru's exercise of their customary rights, judging that Meru practices were incompatible with their own scientific management methods.

Chapter 23, Geography for Life Activities, continued

Conservation or Conceit?

Meanwhile, back in England, politically powerful conservation groups, particularly the Society for the Preservation of the Fauna of the Empire, were lobbying hard for the creation of African national parks modeled on Yellowstone and other American national parks. These parks would implement a mythical vision of Africa as an unspoiled wilderness, where nature existed undisturbed by destructive human intervention. The reality was that thousands of Africans lived in and/or used the resources of the proposed parks. The first park designated under the 1948 National Parks Ordinance was Serengeti, an area of undulating plains with tremendous wildlife resources, including the big game animals. But what should be done with the Masai who lived and grazed cattle in the park? Some whites thought that their presence in the park was fine, so long as they remained "primitive," and could be considered just another part of the fauna. Over time, many relocations were required and rights of access and use were eroded, always without consulting the people affected. Eventually, in 1959, a new National Parks Ordinance (Amended) was passed, and it made clear that there was no place for African peoples or their traditional rights in national parks.

After independence in 1961, international conservation organizations worked with Tanganyika (Tanzania) to continue its program of establishing and managing national parks. The national government saw tourism as an important sector of the economy and knew that tourists wanted to see African wildlife. The government was willing to create parks and evict people from them because parks meant economic development. It has taken several decades for the pay off to occur, in part because so many companies organizing safaris were headquartered in Kenya, where much of the money stayed. Profits from the increased tourist development of recent years go mostly to foreign-owned companies and the national government. Local people bear the costs of the national parks, but do not receive the benefits.

The National Park Today

Arusha National Park was created through a series of acquisitions in the 1960s and 1970s. While many customary rights had been lost in previous decades, the Meru were permitted to continue keeping bees in the park and using a long-established path to move cattle and crops across the park (a two-hour trip instead of the 12-hour one it would otherwise be). These rights were later taken away. In addition, the expansion of park boundaries has brought them right up against cultivated areas, with no buffer in between. As a result, there are serious problems with wildlife destroying crops and animals and threatening human life. The sheer loss of land to the park (and prior to that to white settlers) becomes more critical with Meru population growth. Finally, park managers have made it hard for Meru elders to conduct traditional rituals at a sacred place within the park. Yet at the same time they want to develop the site as an attraction for foreign tourists.

Ironically, preventing the Meru from grazing animals and burning in the park has brought some undesirable vegetation changes, such as more brush. Now the park administration hires Meru people to cut and burn the brush because it obscures tourists' views of the wildlife! Other undesirable changes in the ecological status of the park include reduced numbers of major animal species, including the complete disappearance of the rhinoceros. No major ecological research has been conducted in the park in 30 years, so that it is hard to know who or what is to blame.

The Meru continue to try to obtain basic resources from the park despite the illegality of doing so. Typical crimes are fuel wood collection, trapping for meat, grazing trespass, and cutting of grass for livestock fodder or roofing. Encroachment, whereby farmers expand their plots into the park along its boundary, is also a problem. These acts are a form of resistance to state conservation policies that have resulted in the loss of rights to land and resources. While conservationists see Arusha National Park as a kind of unspoilt Eden that can provide visitors (mostly foreigners) with a sense of primordial nature, for the Meru it is very much a humanized place, one that history shows is theirs and that today can still contribute to their material well-being. What park officials and conservationists view as crimes (against nature and against the government) are thus seen by the local inhabitants as morally justifiable.

Tensions are intensified because the Meru feel that park personnel place the rights of wild animals over those of people. One resident explained, "If an elephant comes into my shamba and pulls up my banana plants, the guards don't do anything. But if a cow takes one step inside the [park] boundary, the guards come and fine the owner." Another man explained, "They [park employees] don't come to help us with the problem of [predatory] animals, so why should we help them? We aren't going to help them catch poachers."

You Are the Geographer

As you can see, local Meru people view Arusha National Park in Tanzania very differently from park administrators, conservation advocates, and visitors. Working alone or in groups according to the wishes of your teacher, come up with some way to vividly communicate these different meanings of place. You should look to the arts for ideas. Possibilities include poetry, a short story, a short play, a song, a painting, or a drawing. Be sure the "voices" of all groups involved, including the wildlife, are represented. Class discussion could center on ways of resolving some of the tensions that have arisen from differing place perceptions. Visual images of Arusha National Park are available on the Internet.

ACTIVITY (24)

National Geography Standard 1

Geography for Life Activities

The Geography of Childhood Deaths in Zimbabwe

Medical geographers study patterns of health and disease. They compare maps showing the distribution of people or animals with a particular illness to maps of other phenomena that might be related. When they see relationships, they initiate further investigations to implement better disease control. Medical geographers also look at the spatial distribution of health care delivery. They analyze the locational patterns of facilities such as clinics and hospitals. They can help devise a network of locations that is cost efficient and that fairly serves a needy population.

A good example of medical geographers at work is schistosomiasis outbreaks. Medical geographers prepared maps that showed that outbreaks of schistosomiasis in Africa and South America often followed the construction of reservoirs and irrigation projects. Schistosomiasis, a disease that causes internal bleeding and fatigue, is caused by parasites that spend part of their life cycle in aquatic snails. When engineers turned rivers into reservoirs, they created more desirable environments for the snails. To take another example, geographers can predict how wind-borne diseases like hoof-and-mouth disease will move. Weather patterns, terrain, and the movements of animals and people are taken into account. This valuable information helps government authorities control outbreaks.

You Are the Geographer

In this exercise, you will prepare a map of childhood mortality (death) rates in Zimbabwe and then examine variables that might help you understand the map. The information in this exercise comes from the work of Tapiwa Jhamba.

1. You need to prepare your map. Table 1 at the end of this activity contains estimates of Zimbabwe's mortality rate by province and district for children under the age of 5 years for the year 1988. Zimbabwe as a whole had a rate of 84. This means that 84 children under five years of age died in 1988 for every 1,000 children of that age in the country. The range of rates in Zimbabwe at the district scale was from 39 (in Matobo) to 155 (in Chipinge). By comparison, the United States had a rate of about 2 per 1,000 in 1990.

The district variations in childhood mortality can be classified into five categories: very low, low, average, high, and very high mortality. The very low category includes districts with rates that were more than 25 percent below the national average. The low category includes districts whose estimates were between 11 and 15 percent below the national average. The average group includes districts whose estimates were within 10 percent of the national average. The high group includes districts with estimates that exceeded the national average by between 11 and 25 percent. The very high group includes districts with rates that were more than 25 percent above the national average.

Calculate your class intervals. For example, the very low category will include districts with rates below 63 per 1,000 [84 − .25(84) = 63]. Then assign each district (and Bulawayo and Harare provinces) to its proper category. Next, devise your symbols. Pick a scheme of colors, shades, or patterns that goes from light to dark. Assign the lightest symbol to the "very low" category and the darkest to the "very high" category. Apply them to the map provided on the next page.

2. On a separate piece of paper discuss the spatial patterns of childhood mortality that you see on your map. Now think about what factors might lay behind those patterns.

3. Study the small map of altitude classes in Zimbabwe shown below. What relationship do you see between it and your map of childhood mortality? The relationship has to do in part with malaria. The lower-lying, higher-temperature regions are more conducive to the mosquitoes that spread malaria. Childhood deaths from malaria are a major reason for Africa's low life expectancies. Write a paragraph about altitude, malaria, and childhood mortality rates in Zimbabwe.

4. Childhood mortality rates (or infant mortality rates) often are used as a measure of socioeconomic development. Find maps of Zimbabwe in your textbook or atlas. Look for cities, roads, and railroads, as these are indicators of development (urbanization and industrialization). Where these are concentrated is the core of the country; elsewhere is the periphery. Is there a relationship between the core and low rates of childhood mortality and the periphery and high rates of childhood mortality in Zimbabwe? What are some reasons for why children are more at risk of dying "out in the sticks"? Consider services, facilities, and attitudes that are more prevalent in cities than in the countryside in formulating your answer. Can you think of any other variables not mentioned above that might influence the pattern of childhood mortality, such as cultural or religious factors? Discuss these.

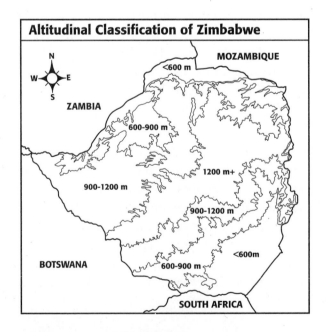

Altitudinal Classification of Zimbabwe

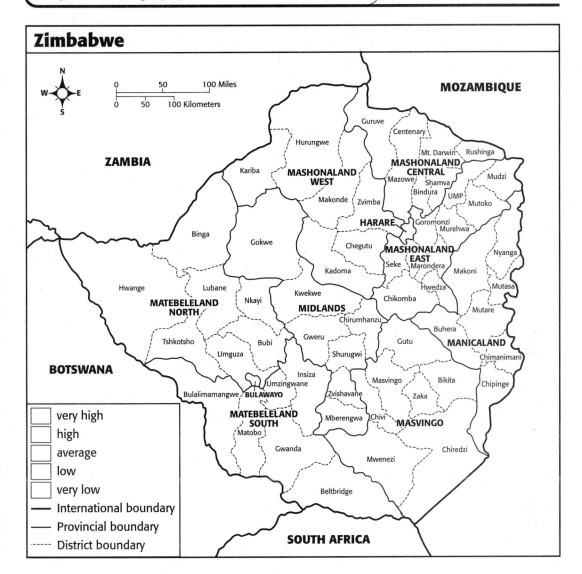

Zimbabwe

ZAMBIA

MOZAMBIQUE

0   50   100 Miles
0   50   100 Kilometers

Guruve

Centenary

Hurungwe

Mt. Darwin   Rushinga

Kariba   **MASHONALAND WEST**   **MASHONALAND CENTRAL**   Mudzi

Mazowe   Shamva

Makonde   Zvimba   Bindura   UMP   Mutoko

Goromonzi   Murehwa

HARARE

Binga   Gokwe   Chegutu   **MASHONALAND EAST**   Nyanga

Seke   Marondera   Makoni

Kadoma   Hwedza   Mutasa

Hwange   Lubane   Kwekwe   Chikomba   Mutare

Nkayi   **MIDLANDS**   Chikomba

MATEBELELAND NORTH   Chirumhanzu

Buhera

Tshkotsho   Gweru   Gutu   **MANICALAND**

Bubi   Shurugwi   Chimanimani

Umguza   Insiza   Masvingo   Bikita   Chipinge

Bulalimamangwe   Umzingwane   **BULAWAYO**   Zvishavane   Zaka

MATEBELELAND SOUTH   Mberengwa   Chivi   **MASVINGO**

Matobo   Gwanda   Chiredzi

Mwenezi

Beltbridge

BOTSWANA

SOUTH AFRICA

	very high
	high
	average
	low
	very low
▬	International boundary
—	Provincial boundary
----	District boundary

Chapter 24, Geography for Life Activities, continued

Table 1. Zimbabwe: Province and District Estimates of the Under-Five Mortality Rate (per 1,000), 1988

Province/District		Province/District		Province/District	
Mashonaland Central	*109*	*Mashonaland North*	*67*	*Manicaland*	*115*
Rushinga	141	Binga	125	Chipinge	155
Centenary	131	Lupane	63	Buhera	119
Guruve	125	Hwange	57	Nyanga	117
Shamwa	115	Umguza	55	Mutasa	110
Mt. Darwin	103	Bubi	55	Chimanimani	98
Bindura	95	Nkayi	55	Mutare	95
Mazowe	89	Tsholotsho	50	Makoni	80
Mashonaland West	*91*	*Matebeleland South*	*56*	*Mashonaland East*	*81*
Kariba	105	Beitbridge	91	Mudzi	94
Hurungwe	101	Insiza	61	UMP	93
Zvimba	96	Bulalimamangwe	51	Murehwa	80
Makonde	90	Gwanda	51	Mutoko	79
Chegutu	82	Umzingwane	43	Goromonzi	78
Kadoma	80	Matobo	39	Marondera	77
				Hwedza	75
Midlands	*84*	*Masvingo*	*95*	*Seke*	*75*
Gwokwe	114	Chiredzi	117	Chikomba	74
Mberengwa	82	Bikita	106		
Zvishavane	76	Mwenezi	102	*Harare*	*59*
Chirumhanzu	74	Zaka	97	*Bulawayo*	*43*
Kwekwe	73	Gutu	84		
Shurugwi	67	Chivi	82	*Zimbabwe*	*84*
Gweru	58	Masvingo	77		

Notes: Estimates are based on the verbal reports of women aged 25–29 on the survival of their children. With the exception of Harare and Bulawayo, the urban centers were combined with the rural districts in which they are geographically located.

Source: Jhamba, Tapiwa. 1999. "Regional Variations in Childhood Mortality in Zimbabwe." *Geography* 84(5): 320.

Name _____ Class _____ Date _____

Geography for Life Activities

National Geography Standard 5   **Linguistic and Political Regions in India**

> *In this exercise, we look at India as we consider states (functional regions) and language areas (formal regions). We will examine the idea that the boundaries between states should correspond to those between language areas, in other words, that functional and formal regions should coincide.*

A region is an area of Earth's surface that is recognized as being different from adjacent areas. There are many ways in which one area differs from another, so there are many possible sets of regions. Regions exist at various scales. Geographers distinguish between formal regions and functional regions. Formal regions, also sometimes called uniform regions, are internally homogeneous in one or more ways. For example, in India, we can identify different areas according to their main subsistence crops. A map of India will reveal that there are rice-growing regions, millet-growing regions, and wheat-growing regions. The sharp lines on maps separating formal regions from one another can be misleading, because in reality the boundaries between such regions often are zones of transition. In these zones, both phenomena, for example, rice and millet, are present to a significant degree.

A functional region is an area organized to facilitate interaction. Typically such interaction is between a central node and a population that is dispersed. Thus "nodal region" is another name for functional region. Political/administrative subdivisions are functional regions and include countries, states, and counties. The central nodes for these are national capitals, state capitals, and county seats. Trade areas are also functional regions. A trade area is the region served by a particular business. Customers come to it or it makes deliveries to customers; either way business and customers are tied together into a functioning spatial unit that makes up a region.

India's Linguistic Diversity

India is linguistically diverse. The 1971 census recorded 281 mother tongues, including 82 with more than 100,000 speakers each. Currently, 18 languages, called "scheduled languages," are recognized in India's constitution as particularly important. From time to time languages are added to this list. Being listed in the constitution confers certain privileges on a language and its speakers. For example, it ensures that federal civil service exams (which provide access to good jobs) will be given in that language. About 96 percent of India's population speaks one of the scheduled languages.

India's languages belong to four language families (see the table and figures at the end of this activity). Nearly three quarters of Indians claim an Indo-European language as their mother tongue, and one quarter claim a Dravidian language. Less than 3 percent have mother tongues from the Austro-Asiatic or Sino-Tibetan families. In the northeastern section of India, linguistic fragmentation is great. This is the part of India dominated by Sino-Tibetan languages, which constitute nearly half of all India's languages, but only

(**Chapter 25, Geography for Life Activities, continued**)

1 percent of speakers. Thus, there is no dominant language in the states of Arunachal Pradesh, Nagaland, Mizoram, Tripura, Meghalaya, or Sikkim. (While your map shows Naga spread over some of this territory, Naga is actually a group of languages, not a single tongue.)

Aligning Languages and Politics

A comparison of the linguistic and political maps of India demonstrates a significant degree of correlation. This was not always the case. When India gained independence from Great Britain in 1947, it was made up of 11 British provinces and 562 autonomous princely states. India acted quickly to consolidate these into 27 territorial subdivisions. Some state boundaries at that time followed language boundaries. Many of the boundaries that did not have since been adjusted to do so. Because of its linguistic diversity, India has experienced considerable conflict over the issues of official languages and language education. The constitution, adopted in 1950, declared Hindi to be the official and national language for the federal government. English was also recognized as a sort of associate official language, but it was supposed to lose this status in 1965.

Hindi is the language spoken by far more Indians (over 40 percent) than any other, and many other Indian languages are closely related to it. Spoken Urdu, which is closely associated with India's sizable Muslim minority, is mutually understandable with spoken Hindi, although they are written in different scripts. Hindi also has the advantage of being the dominant tongue in the political core of India, where the national capital, New Delhi, is located. A problem with Hindi being the official language, of course, is that nearly 60 percent of Indians do not speak it. Non-Hindi speaking Indians also perceive the preference given to Hindi as a disadvantage to themselves.

English was not phased out in 1965 as planned. Less than 5 percent of Indians are fluent and literate in English. Those that are, however, make up the country's educated elite. High-level government administrators are very likely to know English and to use it to communicate in situations where both parties do not know Hindi. (Each state in India has its own official language or languages, and many of them have not chosen Hindi.) English has the advantage of being a truly international language, giving its speakers an advantage in competing for jobs in the globalized economy. On the other hand, English is still resented as the language of colonial oppression.

Government policy states that children should study their mother tongue, Hindi, and English. If their mother tongue is Hindi, then they are to study another Indian language as their third language. This policy is not enforced everywhere, and in some places, the teaching of Hindi is intentionally ignored. Educated Indians are usually multilingual, and even people with little education can often speak a second language.

You Are the Geographer

1. Compare Figure 1, the map of language regions, and Figure 2, the map of states. (Figure 2 shows only India's 25 states, and not its six small Union Territories or the National Capital Territory.) Next to each language in Table 1, write the name of the

Chapter 25, Geography for Life Activities, *continued*

state where it is dominant. Hindi will have three states, and Urdu, Sindhi, Nepali, and Sanskrit will have none. All others will have one state corresponding to one language in the table. Of course, each of these states also has many minority languages.

2. Write a paragraph about what you think are the pros and cons of using language boundaries as the basis for political boundaries between states. While the idea has tended to be popular with the Indian people, national political leaders often have resisted it. Why might that be?

3. Now organize your class into three groups. One group will argue for Hindi as the official/national language, one for English, and one for Hindi and Telugu (the Dravidian language with the most speakers, about 8 percent of Indians) as co-equal official/national languages. Take some time to examine both sides of the argument for your position.

Table 1. Language Families and Selected Languages in India

Indo-European Family (Indo-Aryan Group)

Hindi* ⟶ _____		_____		_____
Bengali* ⟶ _____	Marathi* ⟶ _____			
Urdu* ⟶ _____	Gujarati* ⟶ _____			
Oriya* ⟶ _____	Punjabi* ⟶ _____			
Kashmiri* ⟶ _____	Sindhi* ⟶ _____			
Konkani* ⟶ _____	Nepali* ⟶ _____			
Assamese* ⟶ _____	Sanskrit* ⟶ _____			
Rajasthani ⟶ _____	Pahari ⟶ _____			
Bihari ⟶ _____				

Dravidian Family

Telugu* ⟶ _____	Malayalam* ⟶ _____
Kannada* ⟶ _____	Tamil* ⟶ _____

Austro-Asiatic Family
Sino-Tibetan Family
   Meithei* ⟶ _____

---

*One of India's "Scheduled Languages"
Sources: Breton, Roland J.-L. 1997. *Atlas of the Languages and Ethnic Communities of South Asia*. Walnut Creek, CA: AltaMira Press.
Schwartzberg, Joseph E., ed. 1978. *A Historical Atlas of South Asia*. Chicago: The University of Chicago Press.

Chapter 25, Geography for Life Activities, continued

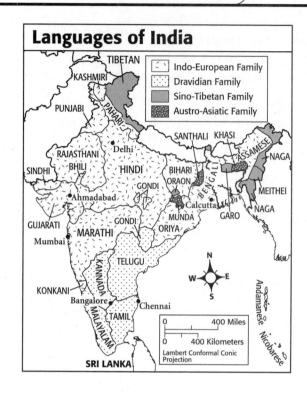

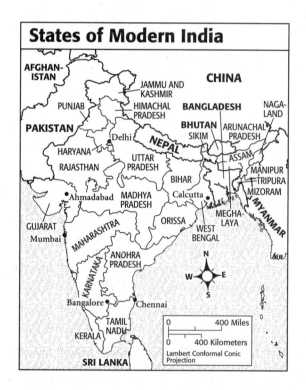

ACTIVITY 26   Geography for Life Activities

National Geography Standard 14   **Irrigation's Impact on Pakistan**

The Indus is one of the world's great rivers, both in size and in significance to humanity. The annual flow of the Indus is twice that of the Nile and three times that of the Tigris and Euphrates combined. Its headwaters are high in the Himalaya Mountains of Tibet. Lower down on its vast alluvial plain, the Indus and its tributaries (the Jhelum, the Chenab, the Ravi, the Beas, and the Sutlej) have enabled humans to create one of world's largest expanses of irrigated agriculture. In this exercise you will learn about the costs and benefits of this endeavor. Consult a map of Pakistan as you read through this exercise.

Except for the highest mountain country, Pakistan is dry. Over two-thirds of it receives less than 10 inches of rain per year. As in all arid places, the rainfall is highly variable and unreliable. For most of the country, about three quarters of the rain falls in the monsoon months of July, August, and September. Summers in Pakistan are very hot, especially on the plains. Evaporation rates are high, and peak in May and June, before the monsoon. Given these climatic conditions, you can see why farmers turn to irrigation.

Irrigation has a very long history along the Indus River, as it has along the Nile and in Mesopotamia. The ancient Indus Valley civilization used the river's natural floods to irrigate adjacent fields of wheat, barley, and rice. The crops were stored in gigantic granaries in cities located along the Indus and its tributaries.

For centuries, Indus Valley farmers irrigated by using inundation canals. These were simple cuts in the banks or natural levees of the rivers, allowing water to flow onto low-lying fields. They could be used only during high water (that is, in the summer when snow melts upstream in the mountains and the monsoon rains arrive), and they were subject to frequent breaks and serious silting up problems. This was the chief irrigation method from the time of the Moghul emperors about five centuries ago until the mid-1800s.

New Irrigation Techniques

In the mid-1800s British engineers started modernizing the old inundation canals and building many new ones. They built weirs and headworks so that water could be retained and diverted year round. In areas where this perennial irrigation became available, two crops a year could now be produced, one harvested in the spring and one in the fall. A severe famine in the northern Indus Plain the the late 1870s spurred the further expansion of perennial irrigation. By the turn of the century the Punjab region fed itself and produced a surplus of food for export.

In the early 1900s, a new scale of water management was undertaken. Because the eastern tributaries could not deliver enough water to irrigate the lands adjacent to them, link canals were constructed. Water was diverted from one river to the next river east, supplying some irrigation water to the land in between on the way.

Upon independence in 1947, Pakistan and India were partitioned. Each country ended up with some of the land watered by the Indus and its tributaries. In 1960, India and Pakistan signed the Indus Basin Treaty. It gave Pakistan exclusive rights to the waters of the Indus, the Jhelum, and the Chenab. India in turn had exclusive rights to the waters of the Sutlej, the Beas, and the Ravi. Further adjustment and expansion of the canal system in Pakistan (and in India) followed this historic agreement. Additional dams and reservoirs were constructed. Pakistan created, mostly in the provinces of Punjab and Sindh, the largest single irrigation system in the world. There are 36,000 miles of conveyance facilities and about one million miles of watercourses, farm channels, and field ditches! Important social relationships exist among farming households that share watercourses.

Today Pakistan is among the world's leaders in extent of irrigated land (see the table at the end of this activity). It is also one of the countries most dependent on irrigation. Among the top 20 irrigators, only Uzbekistan (88 percent) and Egypt (100 percent) have higher shares of their "arable land and land under permanent crops" irrigated.

The Downside of Irrigation

Irrigation has allowed Pakistan to provide food (the most important staples are wheat and rice) and jobs to millions of people. In fact about two-thirds of Pakistan's 145 million people live in the countryside and are supported by agriculture. It has also allowed the production of major export crops such as cotton and rice. But irrigation has brought with it some serious environmental problems.

Foremost among these problems is salinization, the build up of salt in soils. Irrigated areas in virtually all arid lands experience this problem. About one-quarter of Pakistan's irrigated land has been damaged by salt. Saline soils severely reduce plant productivity, and when salinization becomes too bad, land is simply abandoned. Over the years, Pakistan has been able to add new irrigated land faster than it has abandoned salt-damaged land. Still, it is losing about 25 percent of its potential crop production, worth $2.5 billion, annually to salinization.

Eons ago, the Indus Plain was a shallow sea. When the sea receded, salt remained in the soil and the groundwater. The natural weathering of rock contributed additional salt to the soil. When farmers started irrigating, they made the situation worse in several ways. If you keep applying water to soil without proper drainage, the water table (the upper surface of groundwater) will rise higher and higher. Huge amounts of water seeping from unlined canals contribute to this problem. When the water table gets high enough, water moves upward to the surface by means of capillary action. When it evaporates, dissolved salts are left behind.

The extremely gentle slope of the Indus Plain contributes to the problem of poor drainage and waterlogged soils. Even in well-drained areas, if inadequate amounts of water are applied, salt can accumulate in the root zone. Enough water must be available for an occasional heavy application to leach the salt in the root zone deeper into the soil. On the Indus Plain, enough water has not always been available. (Under natural conditions, floods provided the needed flushing.) The government has chosen to spread the resource widely—but too thinly—because that is the least politically painful strategy.

Chapter 26, Geography for Life Activities, continued

These problems can arise even when good quality water is applied, but they are worse when saline groundwater is used for irrigation, as is the case in parts of the Indus Valley. Certain types of salts in this water also cause chemical changes in the soil that make it less permeable. The water sits on top of the soil and evaporates, never reaching the roots of the plants and leaving behind more salt.

The loss of crops due to salinization means less food and reduced incomes for Pakistani farmers, most of whom work less than five hectares of land. Research comparing villages in areas with low levels and high levels of salinity found much greater poverty and many fewer typical household goods, such as refrigerators or TVs, in the salt-affected villages. The ratio of women to men was much lower, suggesting a higher death rate for women than for men when resources are scarce.

Solving the Salinization Problem

The Pakistani government, Pakistani farmers, and international aid donors have spent enormous sums over many decades trying to solve the salinization problem. Hundreds of thousands of tubewells have been installed. These are equipped with pumps that are used to lower the groundwater level. Surface drains and subsurface tile drains have been built. Some canals have been lined to reduce seepage. These methods have had some success, but are very expensive and must be carried out on a large scale (meaning individual farmers cannot help themselves). While good drainage is necessary to manage the salinization problem, so is adequate fresh water. This may become a problem, given Pakistan's rapid population growth.

Draining the land in order to remove excess water only solves part of the problem. Disposal of the salt-laden and polluted water remains a challenge, despite a plan to build outfall drains to the Arabian Sea. Other water bodies continue to receive some of the tainted water. Manchhar Lake, north of Karachi in Sind Province, is an example. The lake's fish and birds are disappearing. The fishery that supported 10,000 fishing families and their traditional culture is collapsing. Hundreds of families have moved to other wetlands in Pakistan, spreading the ripples of environmenal impact.

Farmers are not entirely dependent on large-scale government programs to manage salinization. Smaller scale methods include adding amendments (gypsum, acids, manure, waste from sugar mills) to the soil to improve soil chemistry and texture, so that water infiltrates and drains more easily. Switching crops to those that are more salt tolerant is another important strategy that is being tried. There are more than 1,500 salt-tolerant plant species in the world, and existing agricultural systems in Pakistan use less than 1 percent of them. Some salt-tolerant trees can provide fuel and fodder and also will lower water tables, thus improving conditions for other crops. Scientists are working on genetically altering some traditional crops to make them more salt tolerant.

You Are the Geographer

Prepare a poster that tells the story of irrigation in Pakistan. It should include a map of Pakistan showing, at minimum, the six major rivers of the Indus Valley and the province boundaries and names. Other relevant features you could include are climate zones and/or some indication of elevations or general landform zones (mountains, hills, plains). Best of all would be a map showing the main canals and dams of the irrigation system. Include on your poster the basic facts of irrigation development and agricultural abundance but also salinization and the efforts to combat it.

Illustrate the poster with your own drawings or pictures from other sources. Make sure your poster makes the point that ever more powerful irrigation technology brought larger harvests but also bigger environmental problems. You might pose the question, "Should Pakistan use genetically modified plants to solve its problem of irrigation-induced salinization?" If your teacher wants you to learn more about irrigation in other parts of the world, pick one of the other countries in Table 1, research its irrigation story, and prepare your poster on it.

Table 1.
Top Ten Irrigators, 1998

Country	Irrigated Land	Arable Land and Land in Permanent Crops	Irrigated Land as Percentage of Arable Land and Land in Permanent Crops
India	59,000	169,500	35
China	52,580	135,365	39
United States	21,400	179,000	12
Pakistan	18,000	22,050	12
Iran	7,562	18,381	41
Mexico	6,500	27,300	24
Indonesia	4,815	30,987	16
Thailand	4,749	20,375	23
Russia	4,663	127,917	4
Uzbekistan	4,281	4,850	88

NOTE: Land is expressed in 1000s of hectares.
Source: *FAO Production Yearbook 1999.*

Name _____ Class _____ Date _____

National Geography Standard 4 **China's Geography of Human Development**

Why are people in some places better off than those in others? This is a funda-mental question for geographers and other social scientists. One way of measur-ing how well off people are has been devised by the United Nations Development Programme (UNDP). The UNDP has developed a Human Development Index (HDI), which combines data on life expectancy at birth, education, and income. It ranks every country in the world according to this index, from highest-ranking (Canada) to lowest-ranking (Sierra Leone). High-ranking places have populations who are long-lived, well-educated, and pros-perous. Low-ranking places suffer from health problems (including violence) that shorten lives, from lack of education, and from poverty. By mapping index values and analyzing the patterns that emerge, geographers are better able to answer this age-old question.

The Human Development Index (HDI) has also been calculated for regions within coun-tries. Table 1 at the end of this activity lists China's provinces in rank order according to their 1995 HDI values. Higher index numbers indicate higher levels of human develop-ment. You will be mapping these HDI values. Divide the 30 provinces into five or six classes. One possible set of class limits is: .800–.899; .700–.799; .600–.699; .500–.599; and .300–.399. Assign a different color or pattern to each class; use darker colors or patterns for higher classes and lighter ones for lower classes. Apply these to the outline map of China at the end of this activity. Give your map a title and legend.

You Are the Geographer

Now that you have completed you map, write an essay explaining your understanding of the patterns it displays. Below are questions and information you should consider in your explanation of China's map of human development. Use the following questions and ideas to help you get started.

1. Take into account China's physical geography. Use maps in your textbook and atlases to examine relationships between climate and human development and elevation and relief and human development. What kinds of physical settings seem to have encour-aged human development and what kinds have held it back? Are there any relation-ships between areas of high human development and certain types of agricultural economy?

2. Values for the components of the HDI—indexes of life expectancy, education, and income (Gross Domestic Product)—are also given in the table. In addition, the estimated provincial populations (for the year 2000) are supplied. Are areas of high human development also those of high population density? Are China's areas of highest human development also where you find its biggest cities?

3. Do you see an overall coastal-interior pattern? If so, what underlies it? Under Mao Zedong, investments were directed away from the coast, in an attempt to punish it for its colonial and capitalist past. They were directed toward the interior, guided by the communist ideals of equal levels of development for all regions. After Mao's death, the "pragmatic moderates" led by Deng Xiaoping realized that China needed to open itself to the rest of the world to prosper. For the past 20 years, tremendous resources from inside and outside of China have been enriching China's Pacific Rim. What are the advantages of the coast for capitalist development?

4. There are millions of Chinese living in other parts of Asia. What might their role be in the map pattern you see? What is different about Xinjiang—what resources does it have to help it overcome the disadvantages of an interior location?

5. The map below shows the percent of each province's population that is ethnic minority. The Han make up 91 percent of the Chinese population; the remaining 9 percent is divided among 55 ethnic minority groups. Eighteen of these groups each have more than 1 million members. Some ethnic minority groups are highly concentrated. In fact, five of China's provinces are called Autonomous Regions in recognition of their association with particular minority groups. The Autonomous Regions and their largest minority groups are: Guangxi (Zhuang, who are related to Thais), Inner Mongolia (Mongols), Ningxia (Hui, who speak Han Chinese but are Muslim), Xinjiang (Uighurs and other Turkic peoples), and Xizang (Tibetans). What can you say about the geography of human development and the geography of ethnic minorities in China?

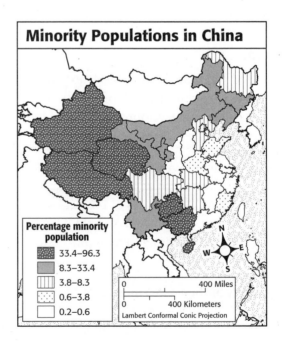

Minority Populations in China

Percentage minority population

- 33.4–96.3
- 8.3–33.4
- 3.8–8.3
- 0.6–3.8
- 0.2–0.6

0   400 Miles

0   400 Kilometers
Lambert Conformal Conic Projection

Name _____ Class _____ Date _____

Table 1. Human Development Index (HDI) and Component Indexes, 1995, and Estimated Population (2000), by Province, China

Rank	Province	HDI	Life Expectancy Index	Education Index	GDP Index	Estimated Population (millions)
1	Shanghai	0.885	0.84	0.85	0.969	17.2
2	Beijing	0.876	0.81	0.86	0.960	14.2
3	Tianjin	0.859	0.80	0.83	0.954	12.4
4	Guangdong	0.814	0.80	0.79	0.850	74.3
5	Zhejiang	0.785	0.79	0.75	0.814	45.4
6	Jiangsu	0.760	0.79	0.77	0.724	41.8
7	Liaoning	0.756	0.76	0.80	0.708	42.8
8	Fujian	0.729	0.76	0.72	0.709	34.1
9	Shandong	0.704	0.77	0.74	0.604	90.9
10	Heilongjiang	0.676	0.72	0.78	0.526	37.7
11	Hainan	0.674	0.79	0.75	0.488	7.3
12	Hebei	0.670	0.78	0.77	0.464	69.8
13	Jilin	0.659	0.72	0.80	0.451	26.7
14	Shanxi	0.627	0.74	0.79	0.352	31.8
15	Xinjiang	0.619	0.67	0.75	0.438	35.4
16	Henan	0.618	0.75	0.74	0.358	93.6
17	Hubei	0.609	0.71	0.73	0.388	59.5
18	Guangxi	0.605	0.74	0.75	0.322	46.4
19	Anhui	0.600	0.75	0.72	0.328	62.0
20	Hunan	0.592	0.71	0.75	0.320	66.9
21	Sichuan	0.582	0.70	0.74	0.308	118.2
22	Inner Mongolia	0.578	0.70	0.74	0.296	27.1
23	Jiangxi	0.577	0.70	0.73	0.327	41.8
24	Ningxia	0.571	0.72	0.67	0.323	5.4
25	Shaanxi	0.570	0.72	0.73	0.259	35.4
26	Yunnan	0.526	0.65	0.64	0.289	40.4
27	Gansu	0.514	0.71	0.62	0.216	24.5
28	Qinghai	0.503	0.61	0.57	0.326	5.1
29	Guizhou	0.594	0.67	0.64	0.172	36.1
30	Xizang	0.391	0.58	0.36	0.226	2.3

Source: Peng, Xizhe and Guo, Zhigang, eds. 2000. *The Changing Population of China.* Oxford: Blackwell.
de Blij, Harm and Muller, Peter. 2000. *Geography: Realms, Regions and Concepts.* 9th ed. New York: John Wiley.

Chapter 27, Geography for Life Activities, continued

Human Development in China, 1995

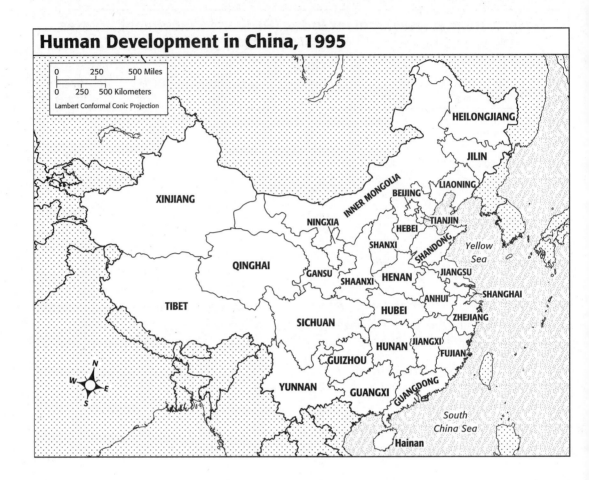

0   250   500 Miles
0   250   500 Kilometers
Lambert Conformal Conic Projection

HEILONGJIANG

JILIN

XINJIANG

INNER MONGOLIA

BEIJING

LIAONING

NINGXIA

HEBEI

TIANJIN

SHANXI

SHANDONG

Yellow Sea

QINGHAI

GANSU

SHAANXI

HENAN

JIANGSU

ANHUI

SHANGHAI

TIBET

HUBEI

ZHEJIANG

SICHUAN

HUNAN

JIANGXI

GUIZHOU

FUJIAN

YUNNAN

GUANGXI

GUANGDONG

South China Sea

Hainan

N
W   E
S

Geography for Life Activities

A Map of Tokyo, A Map of Your Town

On many lists of the world's most populous metropolitan areas, Tokyo comes out on top, with over 34 million inhabitants. This exercise will introduce you to some important places in this gigantic metropolis. It will also give you a chance to try drawing a mental map of your own city or town.

The number of people in Tokyo or any other urban place depends on how you bound it. When it is said that Tokyo has 34 million people, reference is being made to the Greater Tokyo Metropolitan Area (see Figure 1 at the end of this activity). It covers about 13,500 square kilometers (5,215 square miles), encompassing Tokyo Prefecture and three adjacent prefectures, Kanagawa, Saitama, and Chiba. (Japan's prefectures are about the same size as California's counties.) In this exercise we will concentrate on Tokyo Prefecture, especially its eastern portion, which is made up of 23 wards (neighborhood-scale administrative units). The ward area is the core of the metropolis and houses about one quarter of its people. The second map at the end of this activity shows most of the ward area. It is based on a map in geographer Roman Cybriwsky's 1991 book, *Tokyo, The Changing Profile of an Urban Giant*, labeled "Locations of important places in Tokyo."

Tokyo Transportation Nodes

Most Tokyoites move about their city by means of its extensive rail system. The inner part of the 23 wards is crisscrossed by 10 subway lines (not shown on the map). Connecting with the subway are many train lines radiating outward to the suburbs and beyond. The single most important railroad line is the 29-station Yamanote loop. It takes about an hour to ride around it. The most important stations in Tokyo are on this loop where the city subway lines and the suburban rail lines intersect. These include Ikebukuro, Shinjuku, and Shibuya on the west, Shinagawa on the southeast, and Ueno on the northeast. Where the Yamanote line cuts through Tokyo's Central Business District is Tokyo Station, considered to be the city's central railroad station, handling 2,500 trains per day.

Sketch maps of Tokyo, such as those used by advertisers to show customers the locations of their businesses, often include the Yamanote loop. The corridor of the Chuo and Sobu rail lines that cross it is also frequently included. This corridor has a distinctive bend that is readily identified. Virtually all residents look for these features on any map of Tokyo to orient themselves. We could say that the Yamanote loop and the crooked Chuo-Sobu corridor are key elements of the mental maps of Tokyoites.

The Key Districts

Inside the Yamanote loop are many of Tokyo's most famous places. At the heart of Tokyo is the Imperial Palace. The current house of Japan's imperial family is modern, but it sits on the historically important site of Edo Castle. Most of the palace's 45 acres are private green open space that contrasts startlingly with the crowded city around it.

To the south and east of the Imperial Palace is Tokyo's Central Business District (CBD). Geographers use this term to designate a city's core area that has high land values, high concentrations of offices and shops, and high traffic flow. The Yamanote rail loop's Tokyo Station is surrounded by prestige offices, including the headquarters of many of Japan's leading companies. Just to the east is the principal shopping area, anchored by a dozen giant department stores. The Ginza, with its many posh shops and popular nightclubs, is here.

Office buildings are expanding into formerly industrial and warehousing districts along the Tokyo Bay waterfront and the Sumida River. Others are marching toward the western side of the Yamanote rail loop, for several reasons. Tokyo's wealthy suburbs tend to be on this side, and elite residential areas attract prestige offices. Foreign embassies are clustered here, attracting foreign firms and international hotels. The ground is more stable here than on the eastern side of the CBD, where it is reclaimed delta land.

Southwest of the Imperial Palace is the government quarter, where the National Diet Building (the Japanese equivalent of the U.S. Capitol) is the dominant landmark. All of this is visible from another landmark, the Tokyo Tower, an Eiffel Tower look-alike that opened in 1958.

Subcenters have developed around some of the most important stations on the Yamanote loop. Geographers use the term "subcenter" for the many alternative downtowns that have developed in large metropolises. These subcenters are characterized by the same kinds of intense activity, dense building, and expensive real estate as the CBD. On the west side of the Yamanote line, large subcenters have grown up at Ikebukuro, Shibuya, and especially Shinjuku. Office towers, hotels, shopping centers, eating and drinking places, and entertainment venues cluster thickly around these important transit nodes. Tokyo's subcenters, as well as the CBD, include certain areas that are especially popular with young people.

Beyond the Core Districts

Beyond the Yamanote line to the west is the Tama District, where the development becomes more suburban. Land use is increasingly residential, and open space is more common. The suburbs are hardly uniform, however. Some are factory towns with large industrial premises and high-rise housing for workers. Others are college towns. Still others provide mostly single-family housing for people who commute to central Tokyo each day.

Beyond the Yamanote line to the east lies what is left of *shitamachi*, Tokyo's old lowlying rivermouth district, a more humble part of the city. It has changed less than the CBD or prosperous western suburbs, so is sometimes called "the real Tokyo." Older types of housing survive here. There are thousands of "mom and pop" manufacturers and service firms. Tokyo's wholesaling and transport services are concentrated here. There is a huge fish market at the mouth of the Sumida River. The subcenters on this side of the downtown serve a less affluent population than those in the west. The Ueno train station is used by many country people and seasonal laborers. Sanya, Tokyo's skid row, is here. The lower status of this side of town has roots hundreds of years old and is tied to its being a place of disposal, including the disposal of corpses.

Notice the kinds of places located on the map of Tokyo and mentioned in this brief description of its geography. Included are paths (railroads, rivers), nodes (railroad stations), landmarks (Tokyo Tower, the National Diet Building), districts (various wards, the CBD, shitamachi), and edges (the shoreline of Tokyo Bay). These five particular terms were used by Kevin Lynch in his 1960 book, *The Image of the City*. He had residents of Boston draw sketch maps of the city. He identified the common elements among the maps and grouped them into these five categories. Similar exercises have been done since in many other places. The maps that people draw are sometimes called "mental maps."

You Are the Geographer

Much research has been done on how people produce different mental maps of the same place. Mental maps can vary according to people's ages, occupations, genders, lengths of residence, ethnic backgrounds, and social classes. Some cities may be easier to map, too; such cities are sometimes referred to as more legible or more "imageable."

Roman Cybriwsky has some interesting things to say about the mental maps of Tokyoites. He was impressed by the neat and accurate maps that people in Tokyo often draw and give to others, including taxi drivers, to help them find an address. He explains this by pointing out that most streets in Tokyo, other than a few main boulevards, have no names. Addresses are based on a hierarchy of named areas and buildings that are numbered (but not necessarily in spatial sequence). Because of the difficulty of navigating in such an environment, people in Tokyo use maps to a much greater extent than in other places. Their constant use of maps contributes to their being able to draw outstanding sketch maps.

Now try a mental mapping exercise in your class. Have everyone spend 20 or 30 minutes drawing a map of your city, town, or neighborhood from memory. Then compile lists of places (paths, nodes, landmarks, districts, edges) in your locality and tally how many times each appears in your class's set of maps. Why are some places so common, while others rarely or never appear? What differences do you identify among individual maps? How do you explain the differences? Are there any differences between maps drawn by boys and girls? by students with cars and those without cars? by students who have lived locally for a long time and those who have lived locally only briefly? Have a different group (for example, younger students or older adults or students from another school) do the same exercise (given the same amount of time, same size paper, same instructions, etc.). What differences, if any, do you see between their maps as a group and those produced by your class?

Chapter 28, Geography for Life Activities, continued

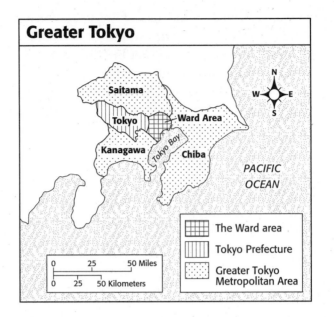

Greater Tokyo

Saitama

Tokyo — Ward Area

Kanagawa — Chiba

Tokyo Bay

PACIFIC OCEAN

The Ward area
Tokyo Prefecture
Greater Tokyo Metropolitan Area

0   25   50 Miles
0   25   50 Kilometers

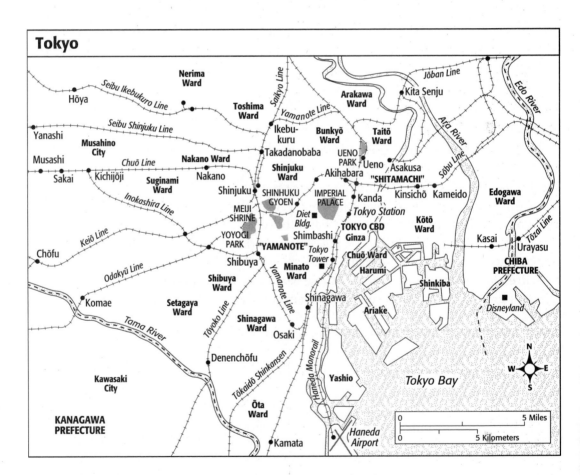

Tokyo

Nerima Ward

Hōya

Seibu Ikebukuro Line

Saikyo Line

Jōban Line

Kita Senju

Edo River

Toshima Ward

Arakawa Ward

Yamanote Line

Seibu Shinjuku Line

Yanashi

Ikebu-kuru

Bunkyō Ward

Taitō Ward

Ara River

Sōbu Line

Musashino City

Musashi

Chūo Line

Nakano Ward

Takadanobaba

UENO PARK

Ueno   Asakusa

Sakai   Kichijōji

Suginami Ward

Nakano

Shinjuku Ward

Akihabara

"SHITAMACHI"

Edogawa Ward

Shinjuku

SHINHUKU GYOEN

IMPERIAL PALACE

Kanda

Kinsichō   Kameido

Inokashira Line

MEIJI SHRINE

Diet Bldg.

Tokyo Station

Kōtō Ward

Tōzai Line

Keiō Line

Chōfu

YOYOGI PARK

"YAMANOTE"

Shimbashi

TOKYO CBD

Ginza

Kasai

Urayasu

Shibuya

Tokyo Tower

Chūō Ward

CHIBA PREFECTURE

Odakyū Line

Minato Ward

Harumi

Shinkiba

Komae

Shibuya Ward

Yamanote Line

Shinagawa

Setagaya Ward

Tōyoko Line

Shinagawa Ward

Osaki

Ariake

Disneyland

Tama River

Denenchōfu

Tōkaidō Shinkansen

Haneda Monorail

Yashio

Tokyo Bay

Kawasaki City

KANAGAWA PREFECTURE

Ōta Ward

Kamata

Haneda Airport

0   5 Miles
0   5 Kilometers

Geography for Life Activities

National Geography Standard 4

**The Shadowed Ground
of Cambodia**

As geographer Kenneth E. Foote discussed in his book, Shadowed Ground, *many places bear the imprint of violence and tragedy. Salem, Massachusetts, Gettysburg, Pennsylvania, and Pearl Harbor, Hawaii, have particular meanings for Americans because of violent events that occurred in those places. Evidence of such events in the landscape includes preserved structures, memorials, and museums. This exercise looks at the evidence of violence that still haunts Cambodia today.*

In the small Southeast Asian country of Cambodia, the violence that has shaped it has only recently ceased. Conflicts devastated Cambodia for the last several decades and left a terrible legacy scattered across the landscape. That legacy is land mines. In many districts, land mines hamper efforts to bring safety and prosperity to the countryside. The precise geography of land mines in Cambodia is unknown. Clearly, that is a big part of the problem. Rumors of land mines are enough to keep people from using a road, cultivating a field, or resettling a village for years.

Understanding the Context

During the Vietnam War, North Vietnamese forces had base camps and supply lines in eastern Cambodia. In an effort to destroy these, the United States covertly carried out massive bombing raids there from 1969 to 1973. Civil conflict also plagued Cambodia during this period. In 1970 the monarch, Norodom Sihanouk, was overthrown by General Lon Nol. Lon Nol's military government engaged in combat with an indigenous Communist guerrilla movement, the Khmer Rouge. In 1975 the Khmer Rouge under leader Pol Pot were victorious.

From the time they took over, the Khmer Rouge engaged in border clashes with the Vietnamese. The Vietnamese invaded Cambodia in 1978 and soon installed a new government. The Khmer Rouge retreated to the Thai border. For the next decade, the Khmer Rouge and several other Cambodian factions fought a guerrilla war against the Vietnamese. The Vietnamese withdrew from Cambodia in 1989 and the United Nations Transitional Authority in Cambodia (UNTAC) was established to oversee democratic elections. Those elections were held in 1993, but there was continued fighting between government forces and the Khmer Rouge. The Khmer Rouge officially reconciled with the Cambodian government only in 1999.

The Land Mine Years

Land mines were first used in Cambodia during the Vietnam War. Both the North Vietnamese and the Americans used antipersonnel mines. Some were scattered from the air during American bombing missions. Later the Khmer Rouge, as they advanced on the capital city, Phnom Penh, mined areas under their control.

The 1979 Vietnamese invasion greatly increased the use of land mines in Cambodia. Huge numbers were used to surround bases and forward posts, to control opposition movement, and to separate opposition forces from their civilian supporters. In 1984 the Vietnamese pushed 220,000 Cambodian fighters and civilians over the border into Thailand. This triggered the creation of the largest minefield in Cambodia, called the K-5 barrier, along the border. For 240 miles, the Vietnamese mined one side and the Thais and Khmer Rouge mined the other. As battle lines shifted, mines were sown on top of mines.

After the Vietnamese left Cambodia, the fighting continued among the Cambodian factions. The various forces used land mines to defend their troops and positions, but also to terrorize and weaken communities outside their control. Mines were laid in rice paddies, forests, roads, railroads, bridges, water sources, irrigation channels, villages, schools, clinics, temples—in short, anywhere. Mining continued during and after the UNTAC period. The government of Cambodia signed the international Mine Ban Treaty in 1997 and ratified it in 1999. There was no documented use of land mines by any armed group in Cambodia in 1999 or 2000.

The Aftermath

The severity of the land mine problem decreases with distance from the Thailand-Cambodia border. The eastern provinces were more affected by unexploded ordnance (UXO) from the Vietnam War bombing than by land mines. *Landmine Monitor Report 2000* noted that 644 square kilometers of Cambodia were known to be mined, and 1,400 were suspected of it. About 155 square kilometers were cleared between 1993 and 1999. No one knows how many mines are involved; one 1998 study estimated 4 to 6 million.

In Cambodia, 85 percent of the population supports itself by farming and related activities. In some areas, land mines have significantly reduced the amount of land available to farmers, thus contributing to poverty and malnutrition. Approximately 110,000 "internally displaced persons" in Cambodia are held back from resettlement by the lack of mine-free land. In places, economically productive activities such as cutting wood or thatch, fishing, and tending animals have been curtailed because of the presence of land mines. Many domesticated animals, especially cows, buffalo, oxen, and pigs, have been killed by land mines, often creating serious economic hardships for the families involved.

Recently, concerns have been raised about wildlife killed by land mines. Another land mine–related environmental problem is the degradation of lands and forests known to be safe. As people avoid mined areas, they put more pressure on a restricted resource base. This problem is worsened by Cambodia's rapid rate of population growth.

The mining of transportation routes impeded the return of refugees and displaced persons and interfered with the economic recovery of the country. Other targets included the cultural treasures of the country, including the great Hindu temple complex Angkor Wat in Siem Reap province. In 1994 Cambodian de-miners, helped by French experts and funding, cleared 1,337 mines and 4,938 UXOs from 24 structures, including temples, pagodas, and schools in the vicinity of Angkor Wat. This kind of effort is required to make Cambodia's most famous tourist attraction safe and thus to rebuild the country's economy.

The number of injuries and deaths from land mines is decreasing, in large part because the fighting has stopped and no new land mines are being used in Cambodia. In 1999 there were 1,012 recorded casualties from land mines, less than one-third the number in 1996. Half of the recorded incidents occurred in Battambang and Banteay Méanchey provinces. During the most recent year-long period for which data are available (June 1999–May 2000), there were 797 casualties. Twenty-six percent of the incidents occurred while the person was farming, 25 percent while traveling, 23 percent while collecting wood or food, 14 percent while tampering, and 5 percent while fishing or herding. One-third of the land mine victims were children.

The Economic Cost

Land mines have burdened Cambodia with tremendous costs. The entire annual budget for national health care in 1999 was $21.1 million for a population of 11.9 million. That works out to less than $2.00 per person. Although medical care is free, many families end up paying privately for care following land mine injuries. Family bankruptcy often follows. Despite help from many international aid donors and nongovernmental organizations (NGOs), many land mine victims in Cambodia do not have access to prosthetic devices, wheelchairs, rehabilitation, mental health care, or job training.

Many millions of dollars and person-hours will be required to de-mine Cambodia. Because of the country's poverty, much of the money has come and will continue to come from abroad. Technological breakthroughs help; for example, the mapping of mine fields can be done more easily now, thanks to global positioning and geographic information systems. Much research is being conducted on mechanical devices that will reduce the danger to human de-miners. But Cambodia's environment offers great challenges to de-mining, with its uneven topography, extensive forests, and high levels of rainfall that wash any rootless thing, including land mines, downhill.

You Are the Geographer

Several activities can build on what you have learned about land mines in Cambodia:

1. One 1995 classification put the provinces of Siem Reap, Banteay Méanchey, Battambang, and Pursat in the "Severely Mined" category. Preah Vihear, Kompong Thom, Kompong Chhnang, Kompong Speu, Koh Kong, and Kampot were considered "Heavily Mined," and Stung Treng, Kratie, Kompong Cham, Kandal, Takeo, Prey Veng, and Svay Rieng "Moderately Mined." Using the map at the end of this activity, choose three colors to designate the three categories of mined areas. Than shade your map accordingly.

2. Work with others to write a short play that tells the story of land mines in Cambodia and warns of their dangers. Such plays have been used in Cambodia for land mine awareness education.

3. Use the Internet to find information on land mines in another country. More than a dozen others are considered severely mined. Write an essay comparing the land mine experiences and issues of that country and Cambodia. Good places to start your search are www.icbl.org and www.landmines.org.

Chapter 29, Geography for Life Activities, continued

Cambodia

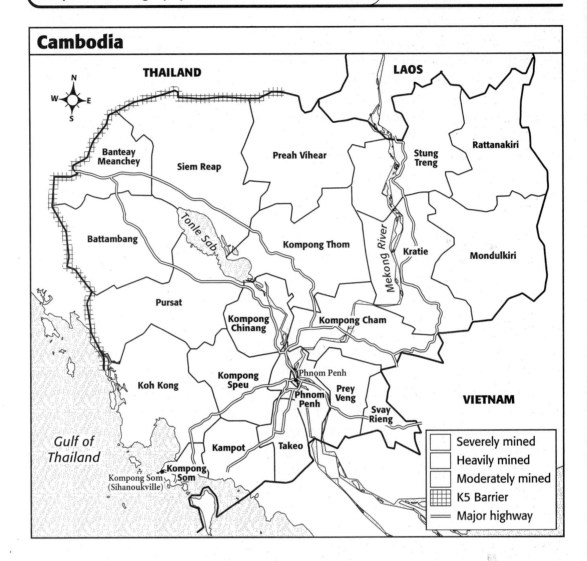

THAILAND

LAOS

Banteay Meanchey

Siem Reap

Preah Vihear

Stung Treng

Rattanakiri

Battambang

Tonle Sab

Kompong Thom

Kratie

Mondulkiri

Mekong River

Pursat

Kompong Chinang

Kompong Cham

Koh Kong

Kompong Speu

Phnom Penh

Phnom Penh

Prey Veng

VIETNAM

Svay Rieng

Gulf of Thailand

Kampot

Takeo

Kompong Som (Sihanoukville)

Kompong Som

	Severely mined
	Heavily mined
	Moderately mined
	K5 Barrier
	Major highway

ACTIVITY 30   Geography for Life Activities

National Geography Standard 7   **Volcanoes in Island Southeast Asia**

Island Southeast Asia is one of the world's most tectonically active zones. Look in your textbook or an atlas for maps of the world's <u>tectonic plates</u> and ocean floors. Just to the east of the <u>Philippines</u> is the deep oceanic <u>Philippine Trench</u>. Such trenches are created as a result of <u>subduction</u>, where the edge of one tectonic plate descends and melts beneath another. In this case, the <u>Philippine Plate</u> is being subducted beneath the <u>Eurasian Plate</u>. West of the Philippines' northernmost large island, <u>Luzon</u>, the Eurasian Plate is being subducted beneath the Philippine Plate. Just south of the islands of <u>Sumatra</u> and <u>Java</u> in <u>Indonesia</u>, the <u>Indo-Australian Plate</u> is being subducted beneath the Eurasian Plate, creating the <u>Java Trench</u>. The world's deepest oceanic trench is the <u>Mariana Trench</u>, south of Japan where the <u>Pacific Plate</u> is being subducted beneath the Philippine Plate. Its lowest point is 36,198 feet below sea level.

The Ring of Fire

Earthquakes and volcanoes are common along the margins of subducting plates. A world map of volcanic eruptions and large earthquakes in historic times will show you their concentration in zones where tectonic plates are colliding. These zones are called <u>convergent boundaries</u>. Much of the rim of the Pacific Ocean lies along convergent boundaries. Because of the many active volcanoes found there, it is known as the <u>Pacific Ring of Fire</u>. Island Southeast Asia makes up part of this Ring of Fire.

Most volcanoes in island Southeast Asia are <u>composite volcanoes</u>, also known as stratovolcanoes. These volcanoes are cones composed of alternate layers of <u>lava</u> and <u>tephra</u>. Lava is magma, or molten material, that flows onto the surface of Earth and then cools and solidifies. <u>Volcanic bombs</u> are viscous lava lumps ejected by an explosive eruption. They become hardened into rounded shapes while in flight. Tephra refers to all sizes of solid material blown out of a volcano. The tephra is ejected by the explosive release of gases under great pressure. The finest particles, which are minute glass shards, are referred to as <u>volcanic ash</u>.

Volcanic eruptions are accompanied by various phenomena that are deadly to humans and destructive to property. <u>Pyroclastic flows</u> are avalanches of hot ash, gas, and rock fragments that roar down the flanks of volcanoes. <u>Mudflows</u> are mixtures of water-saturated mud and debris that move down slope under the force of gravity. Sometimes the Javanese term <u>lahar</u> is used for volcanic mudflows. Lahars contain at least 40 percent (by weight) volcanic ash and rock fragments, making them dense and viscous like wet concrete, yet they flow faster than streams. The French term <u>nuée ardente</u> is used for glowing clouds of hot volcanic ash and gas. <u>Tsunamis</u> are mighty sea waves triggered by earthquakes or volcanic eruptions.

Millions of people in island Southeast Asia live in places subject to these hazards. On volcanoes, people find soils rich in minerals, forests with plant and animal resources, and some relief from the tropical heat. Avoiding volcanic hazards is not easy; even settlements in low-lying coastal zones are subject to tsunamis. The populations of Indonesia and the

Philippines are large and growing; in the next 50 years, Indonesia is expected to add another 100 million people and the Philippines another 50 million. This means more people in the paths of volcanic destruction.

According to *Volcanoes of the World*, a comprehensive catalog of volcanic eruptions during the last 10,000 years, Indonesia leads the world in many volcano statistics. It has the largest number of historically active volcanoes (76), and the second largest number of dated eruptions (1171, compared to Japan's 1274). It has suffered the highest numbers of eruptions with fatalities and damage to arable land. It also has the highest numbers of eruptions that have produced mudflows, pyroclastic flows, and tsunamis. Indonesia has had many more volcano-related evacuations recently than any other nation, including 17 with evacuees numbering in the thousands.

Volcanic Explosions in Indonesia

Two of the most famous and deadly volcanic eruptions of the 1800s occurred in Indonesia. In 1815, Tambora on the island of Sumbawa erupted catastrophically, pouring out huge quantities of ash. An estimated 10,000 people died from falling tephra, pyroclastic flows, and tsunamis. An additional 82,000 on Sumbawa and neighboring Lombok died from subsequent famine and disease. In Europe and North America, 1816 was called "the year without a summer." Snow fell in New England in June. Temperatures dropped as suspended volcanic particles reduced the amount of incoming solar radiation reaching the earth.

Krakatau (Krakatoa) is an island volcano in the Sunda Strait between Sumatra and Java. In 1883 it erupted with tremendous violence. Approximately 36,000 people died, several thousand from pyroclastic flows and the rest from a huge tsunami that swept the shores of Java and Sumatra, reaching elevations above 100 feet. The tsunami was probably triggered by the collapse of the volcano following its explosion. This collapse created a caldera, a gigantic basin with steep walls, which in the case of Krakatau, is largely under water. Atmospheric effects from volcanic material suspended in the stratosphere, such as odd colors and halos around the Sun and moon and spectacular sunsets, were visible around the world for months afterward. Such effects were noted in European poetry and painting of the period.

In the 1900s, three volcanoes in Indonesia each killed more than 1,000 people. These were Kelut and Merapi on Java and Agung on Bali. Pyroclastic flows, nuées ardentes, and lahars all were involved.

Eruptions in the Philippines

The Philippines has had many fewer eruptions than Indonesia (in part because it is only one-sixth its size), but higher *proportions* of its eruptions in the last 10,000 years have involved fatalities, damage to arable land, mudflows, and tsunamis. Thirteen percent of Philippine eruptions have involved human deaths, and 22 percent caused damage. Taal and Mayon volcanoes on Luzon have had especially high human impacts, including about 5,000 deaths in the last 200 years. These resulted mostly from pyroclastic flows and lahars. The latter are triggered by heavy monsoon rains from June to October, sometimes enhanced by rain from typhoons.

Mt. Pinatubo, about 50 miles northwest of Manila on Luzon, erupted on June 15, 1991. It was the second largest volcanic explosion in the world during the 1900s and by far the largest to affect a densely populated area. For several months before June 15, the volcano provided warnings of an impending eruption. Evidence included swarms of earthquakes, powerful steam explosions that blasted three craters on the volcano's north flank, and the venting of thousands of tons of sulfur dioxide gas. These signals, together with evidence of large explosive eruptions in the past, enabled scientists to forecast the eruption. This saved thousands of lives and $250 million in property. Despite evacuation and rescue efforts, about 350 people died from the volcano's catastrophic eruption (many from roofs that collapsed under the weight of wet ash) or from lahars in the first month following the eruption. Another 450 had died by September 20 from disease in evacuation camps.

Mt. Pinatubo's eruption ejected more than one cubic mile (5 cubic kilometers) of material. The ash cloud rose 22 miles (35 kilometers) into the air. Volcanic ash was blown in all directions by intense winds accompanying a typhoon that happened to strike the Philippines at the same time as the eruption. Pyroclastic flows roared down the mountain. Some valleys were filled with volcanic deposits 660 feet (200 meters) thick. So much magma and rock was blown out of the volcano, that its summit collapsed and formed a caldera 1.6 miles (2.5 kilometers) across. A lava dome was built in the new caldera by fresh magma rising toward the surface. Lava domes are steep-sided domes of thick lava extruded from a volcanic vent.

The main post-eruption hazard was lahars. Conditions on Mt. Pinatubo are ideal for lahars. Average annual rainfall ranges from 80 inches on the mountain's northeast flank to more than 160 inches on its summit and southwest flank. Most of this precipitation is concentrated in the season of the southwest monsoon, which is also when typhoons are most likely. Rainfall can be as intense as two inches per hour. Thirty inches can fall in one 24-hour period. The runoff from such downpours easily picks up the unconsolidated volcanic deposits and transports them downhill in the form of rapid and destructive lahars. The amounts involved are staggering. Tens of millions of cubic yards of mud were moved in a single day. While pyroclastic flows reached about 10 miles from the volcanic vent, lahars extended as far away as 30 miles. Lahars from Mt. Pinatubo's 1991 eruption covered hundreds of square miles of land and numerous settlements under many feet of mud.

More Than One Impact

The impacts of Mt. Pinatubo on people have been diverse. Hundreds of people have lost their lives in lahars or in floods worsened by the lahar deposits that occupy riverbeds. These problems are expected to continue for at least several more years as huge amounts of volcanic mud continue to move downhill. Thousands of people lost their homes and productive farmlands. Some have returned to their former villages and fields, and are engaged daily in the process of adapting to the changed conditions. One small example of this is the construction of new homes on stilts, to allow mud to pass underneath. Other people were resettled in new areas, some hundreds of miles away.

One group greatly affected by the eruption were the Aeta, an ethnic minority group of hunter-gatherers living on the forested upper slopes of the mountain. The displacement they experienced has resulted in closer contacts with the majority society. One Aeta woman interviewed for a story in the *Philippine Inquirer* newspaper perceived benefits from resettlement. They included more attention from political leaders, enhanced status for women, and better educational opportunities for children. Another positive development following the eruption was the development of ecotourism on the mountain, as many visitors come to see what happened.

On the other hand, problems remain a decade after the eruption. Thousands of families are still awaiting resettlement, and destroyed infrastructure has not been repaired or replaced. Many people are still threatened by dangerous lahars and floods, despite major emergency preparedness campaigns and enhanced monitoring systems.

You Are the Geographer

Construct a crossword puzzle using the underlined place names and terms. If available, computer software can be used, or your puzzle can be laid out on graph paper. If you need more information for your clues, *Webster's Geographical Dictionary* is helpful for places, and physical geography texts will give you additional information on terms. There are many good books and websites on volcanoes. Some of your clues might require the use of an atlas to solve. For example, your clue could be the latitude and longitude of a particular feature. Stick to the theme of this puzzle as much as possible when adding words not in the exercise. Finally, try completing someone else's finished puzzle.

National Geography Standard 3

Geography for Life Activities

Where Should New Zealand's Urban Areas Be?

Every country has an urban system. An urban system is a set of cities and towns that are linked together by flows of people, money, and ideas. All places in an urban system are not alike. The most obvious way in which they vary is size. Most urban systems are pyramidal. At the top there are a few really big places, at the bottom there are many small places, and in between there are moderate numbers of medium-sized places. Why does such a hierarchy come into being? Why doesn't everyone in the world live in one giant metropolis? Why don't they all live in villages of 500 people?

Theoretically, everyone could live in a single megacity. In reality, that set up would be highly inefficient because the resources that people exploit (sunlight, soil, water, minerals, plants and animals) are spread across Earth's surface. Tremendous time and energy would be spent traveling from home to wherever those resources are located.

On the other hand, we do not all live in villages because there are certain advantages to settlements of larger sizes. For example, there are many goods and services that require large populations to support. A village of 500 cannot support a university, a superregional shopping mall, a symphony orchestra, or a brain surgeon. In the vocabulary of central place theory, these are high-order central place goods and services, and only high-order central places—large metropolitan areas—can support them. While there are many more low-order central places such as villages, each one supplies only low-order central place goods and services, such as gasoline, groceries, and video rental. Whether a good or service is low-order or high-order depends on how many people it takes to support it. As you move from lower orders in the central place hierarchy to higher-order ones, the number of places decreases, while their spacing (distance from other central places of the same order) increases, as does the variety of goods and services they offer.

The Functions of Urban Spaces

In addition to size, urban places also vary by function. While virtually all urban places are central places, many also perform other functions. Cities are sites for company headquarters, research and development activities, manufacturing, warehousing, transportation facilities, tourism, and government. While urban areas, especially large ones, tend to have a mix of these economic activities, they often are somewhat specialized, too. In other words, cities often have more than their "fair share" of certain types of jobs. New York City, Washington, D.C., Detroit, San Jose, and Orlando are examples. Cities become specialized in particular functions in part because of certain resources in their regions. Can you name the resources that gave each of the above cities their specializations?

In some countries, one metropolis dominates the urban hierarchy. Such a place is called a primate city. One rule of thumb is that the largest place in an urban system is a primate city if its population is quite a bit larger than twice that of the second largest place. A primate city typically has not only a large share of its country's people, but also of its economy, political power, and cultural institutions. Small countries are more likely to have a primate city system than are large ones. That makes sense, because if you have only a few million people, once you have concentrated your population and other resources in order to be able to support very high-order urban functions, you may not have enough "left over" to completely fill out your urban hierarchy.

You Are the Geographer

In this exercise you will invent an urban system for New Zealand. Background information on urban systems and mapped information on New Zealand are provided. Use the maps at the end of this activity, but do not look at any maps of New Zealand that show its actual cities and towns. Additional maps of various physical features (topography, climate, resources) are fine. You are looking for information that will help you decide where to locate New Zealand's top 15 cities, whose sizes and functions (for example, national capital, corporate headquarters city, tourist mecca, manufacturing center, major port) as well as locations, are up to you.

Keep in mind several things as you locate your cities. You need medium-sized central places to serve all parts of the islands. You need ports, as trade is very important to New Zealand. You need manufacturing centers to process New Zealand's natural resources and farm output. You need a city where big banks and corporations have their headquarters. You need university towns, as this is a well-educated country. Tourism is important too. You need a national capital.

In 2000 New Zealand had about 3.8 million people. About 2.7 million lived in its top 15 urban places (called "main urban areas"). The total population of your hypothetical 15 urban places taken together should also be 2.7 million.

Indicate the locations, sizes, and functions of 15 urban areas on the blank map of New Zealand at the end of this activity. For each of the 15 areas, write a sentence or two about why a city of that size and specialization makes sense in that particular location. After you have done that, consult maps of New Zealand and a source (such as *Webster's Geographical Dictionary*, *The Reader's Digest Guide to Places of the World*, an encyclopedia, or sites on the Internet), that gives basic information on places. Compare New Zealand's actual set of 15 largest urban areas with the one you invented. How are their locations and functions similar and how are they different and why?

Chapter 31, Geography for Life Activities, continued

Elevation and National Parks

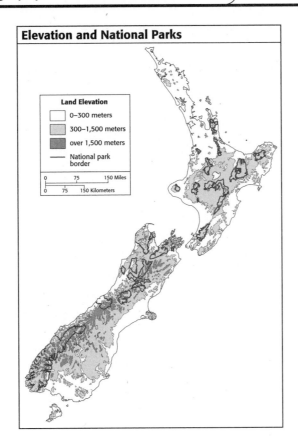

Land Use and Mineral Resources

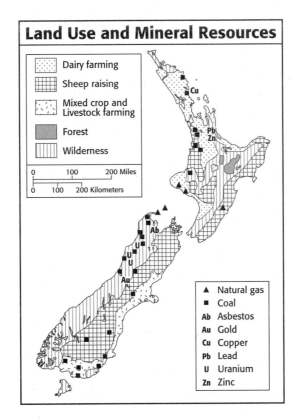

Name _____ Class _____ Date _____

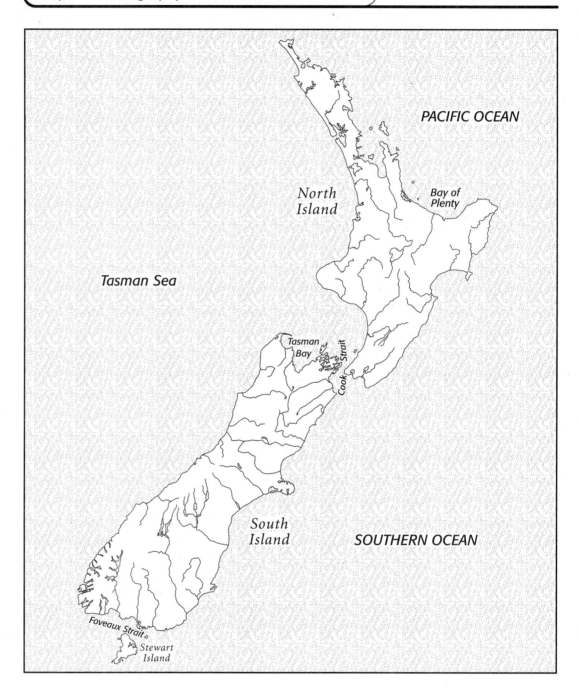

PACIFIC OCEAN

North
Island

Bay of
Plenty

Tasman Sea

Tasman
Bay

Cook Strait

South
Island

SOUTHERN OCEAN

Foveaux Strait

Stewart
Island

Name _____ Class _____ Date _____

Geography for Life Activities

Biogeography of the Pacific Islands

Biogeography is the study of the spatial distribution of plants and animals. By comparing maps of various species and aspects of the environment, such as climate and soils, scientists can begin to see their interrelationships. Seeing how species alter their distributions over time can shed light on both environmental change and evolution of species. The theory of continental drift is supported by maps of reconstructed ancient plant and animal distributions.

Many scientists interested in natural history (a term used for the study of nature before the emergence of specialized disciplines) in the 1800s did biogeographical work. And because the 1800s were a time of exploration of the Pacific Ocean, many of them worked there. Building on the base established by these pioneers, much has been learned about the biogeography of Pacific islands. One question that has been addressed by many researchers is, "how can we explain the variation in numbers of species on different islands?" In general, the tropics have the the greatest diversity of species in the world. This diversity is explained with reference to the ready availability of solar energy and water there, in contrast to colder or drier places. However, within the region of the tropical Pacific, there are islands with few species, as well as islands with many.

What Contributes to Diversity?

One relevant factor is island size. Large islands tend to have more species than small ones. This is not only a function of the amount of space available, but of the fact that the larger an island is, the more likely it is to contain different kinds of environments. With a variety of environments will come a variety of flora and fauna.

Many of the smaller islands of the Pacific are atolls—low-lying ring-shaped islands made of coral resting on a seamount or other submarine structure built up from the ocean floor. Generally, the sandy soil of atolls is not very fertile, nor is it good at retaining water. Typically, the small size and limited resource base of low islands limits their biodiversity.

The Pacific's less "altitudinally challenged" islands are referred to as high islands. Some are oceanic and others continental. Oceanic high islands result from volcanic activity on the ocean floor without any geological link to larger land masses. Oceanic high islands are found throughout Micronesia and Polynesia. The largest and youngest oceanic high island in the Pacific is the island of Hawaii. Continental high islands rest on a continental shelf and geologically are parts of continents. Volcanism can be present on such islands too. New Zealand and the large islands of Melanesia, including New Guinea, are continental high islands.

Both oceanic and continental high islands tend to have richer flora and fauna than do low islands. In addition to their often greater size, their variety of elevations creates opportunities for biodiversity. They also capture and retain much more fresh water than atolls, a vital resource to many species.

Connectivity

Continental islands, because they rest on continental shelves, had land bridges to continents or to other islands when sea levels were lower. Plants and animals could cross on these bridges. This was not the case with atolls or oceanic high islands, although chains of islands (past and present) can act as stepping stones. Oceanic islands, high or low, have had to rely on overseas dispersal to receive their flora and fauna. As a result, many such islands lack numerous groups of plants and animals that make poor overseas travelers. Among groups largely missing from oceanic islands in the Pacific are native earthworms, fresh-water fishes, frogs, land snakes, and all mammals except a few bats and small rodents. Many families of flowering plants, especially those with fleshy or heavy fruits or seeds unlikely to survive long trips over water, are significantly few.

Another factor behind the variation in species richness among Pacific islands is distance from source areas. Wallace and many later researchers have noted that islands far from source areas have fewer species than islands near source areas. The main source area from which the thousands of islands of the Pacific have received biota has been New Guinea and the other large Melanesian islands. They in turn share botanical and zoological elements with the Indo-Malaysian region (island and mainland South and Southeast Asia) and Australia. Elements of flora and fauna characteristic of Antarctica during a warmer forested phase can be detected too, as can elements from East Asia, particularly in the more northerly island groups such as the Marianas. How close a particular island is to a particular source region plays an important role in patterns of dispersal. At the same time, it is important to remember that the current distribution of continents and islands was radically different in the past.

Islands everywhere on Earth tend to have high rates of endemism, and islands of the Pacific are no exception. If a species is endemic to a place, that means it is found only there. Unfilled niches and reduced competition on islands encourage new species to emerge, and isolation tends to preserve them. Species that once were more widespread also survive as relict endemics on some islands. New Caledonia, New Zealand, and Hawaii have especially high rates of plant endemism.

You Are the Geographer

1. Now let's try a simple statistical test of the strength of (1) the relationship between an island's number of species and its size, and (2) an island's number of species and its distance from the main source of species. Here we use number of land and freshwater bird species, but many other groups of plant or animals species would do as well.

   To determine if there is any relationship between species and island size, we will construct a formula, known as Kendall's rank correlation coefficient (tau), to measure the degree of association between two variables. Let's calculate it for number of bird species (X) and island size (Y). The values for number of bird species are already in rank order in the table. You must now rank the islands by size. Arrange the ranks of X in natural sequence, setting below each rank the paired rank of Y, as follows:

X	1	2	3	4	5	6	7	8	9	10
Y	2	1	3	4	5	6	9	7	8	10

Table 1. Number of Land and Freshwater Bird Species, Island Size, and Distance from New Guinea for Selected Pacific Islands and Island Groups

Island or Island Group	Number of Bird Species	Size (Sq. mi.)	Distance from New Guinea
Solomon Islands	138	11,500	_____
Bismarck Islands	132	19,173	_____
New Caledonia	71	7,367	_____
Fiji	58	7,055	_____
Vanuatu	57	5,700	_____
Samoa	33	1,209	_____
Tonga	20	270	_____
Society Islands	12	621	_____
Marquesa Islands	11	480	_____
Pitcairn Islands	4	18	_____

Source: Keast, Allen. 1996. "Avian Geography: New Guinea to the Eastern Pacific." In *The Origin and Evolution of Pacific Island Biotas, New Guinea to Eastern Polynesia: Patterns and Processes,* ed. by Allen Keast and Scott E. Miller. Amsterdam: SPB Academic Publishing, and *Webster's Geographical Dictionary.*

We see now that although the Solomon Islands has the largest number of bird species, it is only second in size. Inspect the ranks of Y beginning at the left, in this case with the rank of 2. Record the number of ranks to the right that are greater than 2, allotting each a +1. These are ranks 3, 4, 5, 9, 7, 8, 10, which contribute +8. Then record the number of ranks to the right which are smaller than 2, allotting each a -1. In this case there is only rank 1, which contributes -1. Add the two contributions for rank 2 together, that is, (+8) + (-1) = +7. Adopt the same procedure for each rank of Y. Sum the totals for all ranks of Y to form an over-all total termed S. In this case,

Ranks of Y

2	(+8)	+	(-1)	=	+7
1	+8	+	0	=	+8
3	+7	+	0	=	+7
4	+6	+	0	=	+6
5	+5	+	0	=	+5
6	+4	+	0	=	+4
9	+1	+	(-2)	=	-1
7	2	+	0	=	+2
8	1	+	0	=	+1
10	0	+	0	=	0
			S	=	39

The maximum possible score obtainable in this way—when the ranks form a perfect sequence, is found by the formula $.5N(N - 1)$, where N is the number of ranks. Tau is a measure of the disorder of the ranks of one variable when the other is placed in perfect sequence, and is found from the formula,

$$tau = S / .5N(N - 1)$$

where S is the sum contributed by the ranks of one variable in the way described above, and N is the number of paired ranks.

When both variables have ranks in perfect sequence, that is, when the correlation is perfect, both the denominator and the numerator of the fraction will be equal, yielding a correlation coefficient of +1 or -1, depending on whether S is positive or negative. If our case, tau $= 39/ .5(10)(10 - 1) = .87$. By consulting a table of values of Kendall's Rank Correlation Coefficients, it turns out to be extremely unlikely that such a value is due to chance variations. In other words, the number of bird species and island size are highly correlated.

2. Now use a map of the Pacific island region to find the distances between each island or island group and New Guinea. Measure from the center of New Guinea to the approximate center of each island or island group. Enter these values in the table, and make distance your new variable Y. Calculate tau. How does the correlation coefficient for number of species and distance from New Guinea compare to the one calculated above for number of species and size?

In this exercise, we used a simple technique and small data set. More sophisticated statistical techniques and larger data sets are available to help biogeographers sort out the complex relationships among number of species and various characteristics of islands in the Pacific realm.

ANSWER KEY

Activity 1

1.–3. Students should accurately place the lines of latitude and longitude as well as the locations indicated on their maps.

4. Stockholm, Sweden; Havana, Cuba; Sydney, Australia; Nairobi, Kenya

5. Answers will vary.

6. The Great Circle distance between Dallas and Islamabad is 7,815 miles.

7. On the Mercator projection, Greenland looks slightly larger than South America. In reality, South America has 6.9 million square miles and Greenland has 840,000 square miles. South America is more than eight times larger than Greenland. Because of the Mercator projection's size distortions, dot maps using it will give a false picture of relative densities.

8. Students should accurately complete their grids.

9. E is at T5S, R4E. F is at Section 7, T1N, R4E. G is at the W1/2 of the NW1/4 of Section 22, T1N, R4E. H is at the SW1/4 of the SW1/4 of the NE1/4 of Section 22, T1N, R4E.

10. Accept all reasonable responses.

Activity 2

Answers to model questions:
1. a **2.** b **3.** c **4.** c **5.** b

Activity 3

Accept all reasonable responses.

Activity 4

Accept all reasonable responses.

Activity 5

Index numbers for the 35 metros are: 46.9, 5.3, 54.0, 1.2, 13.7, 10.4, 8.3, 5.5, 18.9, 27.4, 17.6, 13.6, 13.6, 0.9, 7.9, 17.4, 2.7, 3.3, 12.3, 15.4, 5.1, 3.0, 5.7, 10.2, 0.7, 4.0, 0.0, 4.3, 6.1, 2.5, 11.5, 13.6, 9.4, 15.9, 1.8.

1. In general, large cities have high numbers of skyscrapers. A large population is needed to give rise to a sufficient amount of the kinds of activity (mostly prestige office but in some cases prestige hotel and prestige apartments) that can fill a skyscraper. Also, skyscrapers are partly a response to (and also partly a cause of) high land values. These are found only in the largest cities.

2. New York City and Chicago are providing office space to firms with operations around the world. They are part of a set of cities managing the global economy, so the number of skyscrapers they have (or the total prestige office space) is not only a reflection of the local, regional, or even national economy. Los Angeles is not so important as a global headquarters city. It is also a product of the automobile, so its office space is in lower rise structures and spread out across the metropolis to a greater extent than that of New York City or Chicago.

3. They occupy peninsular sites with limited space.

4. Being in the shadow of a larger city would have a dampening effect on skyscraper construction. Firms looking for prestige would be likely to bypass smaller centers in favor of the "big time." Examples: Sacramento in the shadow of San Francisco; Milwaukee in the shadow of Chicago; Portland in the shadow of Seattle.

5. Minneapolis-St. Paul, Denver

6. (a) San Francisco, New York, Chicago, Charlotte (b) Houston, Dallas-Ft. Worth, New Orleans, Denver

7. Pittsburgh. Detroit, Cleveland, St. Louis, Cincinnati.

8. Views. Of the various monuments and public buildings in Washington; of William Penn's statue on top of Philadelphia's city hall (this limit has been lifted); of the beautiful views of the hills and San Francisco Bay.

9. Dallas-Ft. Worth and Houston; San Francisco and Los Angeles; New York and Chicago; Cleveland and Cincinnati (and Columbus!); Kansas City and St. Louis.

10. Accept all reasonable answers.

Activity 6

Task 1. Accept all reasonable responses based on the data from Table 1, but students should mention the change in U.S. dominance of the automobile manufacturing market. The United States has gone from producing more than half of all cars made to just 17.1 percent. However, the actual number of vehicles produced by the United States has not changed significantly. Students should also note the strong increase in production by Japan.

Activity 7

Accept all reasonable responses.

Activity 8

<u>Places and Regions:</u> all place descriptions, including of particular cities or city neighborhoods; observations on changing character of the Mississippi River corridor, such as its former status as French territory, or expectations of future character, such as more people with more liberal social attitudes; Twain suggests the mosquito regions, the tobacco-spitting region (and its shrinkage), regions of Southern romanticism.

<u>Human Systems:</u> The places along the Mississippi are connected by trade and transport. The axis of movement along the Mississippi is N-S, but the westward spread of settlement, aided by the railroad, is creating more E-W movement. Movement is influenced by technology: keelboat, steamboat, railroad and tug-boat.

<u>Environment and Society:</u> The river's constant motion transforms its immediate environment by shifting sediment, cutting banks, depositing snags, etc. Humans have to cope with the natural hazards of the river valley, including flooding, the dynamism of the river, muddy water, and mosquitoes (which carried diseases). Humans used the resources of the corridor, including wood (to power the steamboats). On Twain's 1882 trip, he saw humans managing the river in new ways: lighting it, removing its snags, engineering it; explanations of how cut-offs and tow-heads take away

former river-frontage locations with devastating economic consequences; Minneapolis's location on a falls brings it waterpower and industry.

Activity 9

1. Students should label the provinces accurately.
2. Yukon, Northwest Territories, Nunavut. The subarctic and tundra climates found here are very cold and the growing season is very short. Mining, forestry, fishing, and trapping occur in these areas.
3. For Alberta through Saskatchewan the percentages are 32.9, 2.8, 14.1, 5.4, 0.1, 8.1, 6.1, 46.9, 2.5, 46.6. Apart from Prince Edward Island, the largest percentages belong to Saskatchewan, Alberta, and Manitoba. These three provinces have the largest farm sizes in Canada. Their average size is several times larger than that in the other provinces.
4. Alberta and Ontario generate the largest gross farm receipts. For Alberta through Saskatchewan the percentages are 24.5, 5.7, 9.2, 1.0, 0.2, 1.2, 24.1, 1.1, 15.4, 17.4. Together Alberta and Ontario account for nearly one half of Canada's gross farm receipts.
5. The Atlantic provinces generate 3.5 percent. Not necessarily. An economic activity may be making only a tiny contribution to a larger whole, but it may still be very significant locally.
6. Quebec has the largest number of dairy farms. Ontario is second. Possibilities include Toronto, Montreal, Ottawa-Hull, Quebec, Hamilton, London. These are six of Canada's 10 largest metros. The climate of these two provinces is humid continental with cool summers. Hay and fodder are dairy cattle (and beef cattle) feed.
7. Alberta, Ontario, Saskatchewan, and Manitoba are the top provinces in beef cattle. Alberta, Saskatchewan, and Manitoba more strongly emphasize dairy farming. The climate is drier; part of the Prairie Provinces is in the mid-latitude steppe climate zone. Land that is too dry for many crops can support animals, but

only at relatively low densities, so farms need to be large to be successful.

8. Wheat. Eastern Argentina and southern Brazil; a broad band across Eurasia, from Bulgaria through the Ukraine and Russia to northern China. These regions are important wheat producers.

9. Ontario, British Columbia, and Quebec have the most fruit and vegetable farms. Nova Scotia is fourth ranked. The Annapolis-Cornwallis Valley is in Nova Scotia; the valley of the St. Lawrence River is in Quebec and Ontario; the Niagara Plain is in Ontario; the Okanagan Valley and the lower valley of the Fraser River are in British Columbia.

Activity 10

Students brochures should include all pertinent information. Accept all reasonable responses.

Activity 11

Students' oral presentations on the music of the country they have chosen should include all five elements suggested. Accept all reasonable responses.

Activity 12

1. Montevideo, Uruguay, Stantiago, Chile, and Buenos Aires, Argentina have the highest primacy by the first measure. Buenos Aires, Argentina, Asuncion, Paraguay, and Montevideo, Uruguay have the highest primacy by the second measure. São Paulo, Brazil, Bogota, Colombia, and Caracas, Venezuela have the lowest primacy by the first measure. La Paz, Bolivia, Guayaquil, Ecuador, and Caracas Venezuela have the lowest primacy by the second measure.

The following figures are the percentages of national population captured by each nation's largest city: Argentina, 33.5; Bolivia, 17.4; Brazil, 10.3; Chile, 36.0; Colombia, 14.6; Ecuador, 18.6; Paraguay, 22.1; Peru, 28.5; Uruguay, 40.0; Venezuela, 14.9. The following figures are how many times larger the largest city is than the second largest in the country: Argentina, 8.7; Bolivia, 1.4; Brazil, 1.7; Chile, 15.3; Colombia, 2.1; Ecuador, 1.4; Paraguay, 42.1; Peru, 7.4; Uruguay, 17.0; Venezuela, 1.9.

The colonial economies of Latin America were designed to provide precious metals and raw materials to the mother countries. The goods were collected at a few central points from which they were taken to Europe. Political administration was highly centralized and directed from the top. In neither case, economic or political, was there any intent to develop the colonies into self-sustaining or self-governing units. Primate city systems suited these colonial goals. Many small countries have primate city systems; in order to provide a wide range of specialized goods and services, you need a large city. It then may be hard to develop competing centers with the remaining population. Also, in terms of communications, you may be able to serve all your territory from a single large city, so the impetus to develop regional cities for administrative or distributive purposes is not as great as in large countries.

2. Most large cities are on the coast or coastal plain. This situation again is a legacy of mercantile (trade-based) colonialism wherein cities are break-of-bulk points in a European-dominated trade system. You can see this by looking at the transport systems of Latin America. Since the colonial period, large cities have been well connected to their immediate hinterlands (and by ship to Europe), but not with one another. More recently, countries have been trying to change this pattern. Many interior cities are resource-oriented or have been developed in recent decades as part of regional development programs to tap the interior. Brazil moved its national capital from coastal Rio de Janeiro to interior Brasilia to encourage urban growth there. Another relatively empty area is the southern part of the continent below Concepción. Topography

and climate become challenging there, and it is far away from trade partners. Students can gain further insight on the locational determinants of Latin America's big cities by studying their individual histories and sites and situations (see exercise on the eastern Mediterranean).

Urbanization is accompanied by economic changes away from agriculture and toward manufacturing and services. In general, jobs in manufacturing and services, if they involve some degree of skill, earn higher incomes than do jobs in agriculture. Despite the fact that many rural people in Latin America come to cities only to find themselves unemployed or underemployed, there is enough production occurring in cities to make the more urbanized countries wealthier than the more rural ones (again in general).

American Indians are more likely than other ethnic groups in Latin America to live in rural places and to still be engaged in subsistence agriculture or in a few places, gathering and hunting. Part of this is no doubt due to cultural preference, but some is also attributable to lack of opportunities provided by the dominant culture. Indian rural population patterns and low incomes go together.

Activity 13

1. Europe has about as much forested land as Australia/New Zealand/Japan, but only about two-fifths as much as North America, and one-fifth as much as the Former Soviet Union.

2. Of the four temperate regions Europe has the lowest share of its forest undisturbed. Most of Europe's forests are "semi-natural." Europe and Australia/New Zealand/Japan have the highest shares of their forests classified as "plantations."

3. Europe has the smallest share of its forested land protected by law or economic situation. Europe.

4. Europe has less than half of its forests in public ownership, compared to about two-thirds for North America and Australia/New Zealand/Japan, and

Activity 13 Table 1. Selected Temperate Forest Data by World Region

	Europe*	Former Soviet Union	North America	Australia/ New Zealand/ Japan	Total
Forest Land	175,828	855,740	461,904	188,891	1,682,363
Undisturbed by humans	7,036	750,856	143,157	23,496	924,545
As a percentage of all forest land	4.0	87.7	1.0	12.4	55.0
Semi-natural	156,703	82,305	305,060	152,119	696,187
As a percentage of all forest land	89.1	9.6	66.0	80.5	41.4
Plantations	12,089	22,579	13,687	13,276	61,631
As a percentage of all forest land	6.9	2.6	3.0	7.0	3.7
FNAWS	27,000	309,000	138,000	147,000	621,000
FNAWS as a percentage of all forest land	15.4	36.1	29.9	77.8	37.0
Forest Land in Public Ownership	79,401	855,740	291,824	129,945	1,356,910
Public forest land as a percentage of all forest land	45.2	100.0	63.2	68.8	80.7
Population of region (in 1000s)	585,075	284,112	304,591	148,786	1,322,564
Hectares of forest land per capita	0.3	3.0	1.5	1.3	1.3
Average annual change in forest extent	+500	-520	+590	+40	+610

100 percent for the Former Soviet Union.

5. Europe has by far the lowest amount of forest per capita of the four temperate regions. Australia/New Zealand/Japan has four times as much, North America five times, and the Former Soviet Union ten times. If countries can offset their greenhouse gas production with forested lands, Europe will be at a disadvantage.

6. Sweden, Finland, France, Spain, Germany

7. Finland, Sweden, Slovenia, Estonia, Austria. Finland, Sweden and Estonia are northern countries, where climate discourages agriculture and so helps to preserve the forest. Slovenia and Austria are mountainous countries, where steep slopes and climate discourage agriculture and help to preserve the forest.

8. Most forested land per capita: Finland, Sweden, Norway, Estonia, Lithuania. Least forested land per capita: Netherlands, United Kingdom, Belgium, Denmark, Iceland. The countries with the most forest per capita are all countries of the far north. The least forested countries are the same group as in question 9, except that Belgium replaces Ireland. Ireland's population declined tremendously in the 1800s through famine and emigration.

9. Sweden, Albania, Bulgaria, Finland, Slovenia. Places with lots of forest are more likely to have some remaining undisturbed. Parts of Albania, Bulgaria, and Slovenia are very rugged and remote. Twelve European countries have no undisturbed forest.

10. Ireland, Denmark, United Kingdom, Belgium, Netherlands. These are countries that have relatively little total forest. They were largely deforested, and plantations represent efforts to remedy that situation.

Activity 14

1. The switch away from subsistence agriculture to a commercial economy meant being linked to others became much more important. Only some places, not all, became better linked, and those that did not were at a great disadvantage. People left the most isolated places.

2. The added transport costs would make nonlocal goods and services more expensive and reduce levels of trade. There would be many small businesses with small trade areas and not much competition. This could drive up the cost of local goods.

3. Bridges (examples: Golden Gate, San Francisco-Oakland Bay, Bronx-Whitestone, Triborough) and dams (examples: Hoover, Fort Peck, Grand Coulee).

4. Percentage change for Odense (-50 percent), for Vejle (-37 percent), for Sonderborg (Als) (-30 percent), for Esbjerg (-39 percent), for Århus (-32 percent), for Herning (-44 percent), for Ålborg (-29 percent).

5. Eastern Fyn, including Odense, and southwest Zealand are now more central and can expect more investment and economic growth. Odense might emerge as a place for business meetings. Copenhagen, already Denmark's dominant city, has enhanced its location. North Jutland and Ålborg became even more peripheral. The port functions at Rødbyhavn and Copenhagen may suffer, as more goods move by truck and train and less by ship. The ferry industry will suffer (ferries have been discontinued across the Great Belt). In the short run, the airlines will suffer, as more people take the train or a car, but if fixed links create more trade and spatial interaction in the long run, the airlines may recoup their initial losses as more people travel using all modes of transport. If better connections such as the Great Belt Fixed Link bring more trade, then wholesalers who handle it will benefit.

6. Copenhagen is a bigger metropolis than Malmö, so you would expect it to attract more people. In terms of longer distance travelers, there is more beyond Denmark (to the south) to attract Swedes than there is beyond Sweden (to the north) to attract Danes.

7. Answers will vary but might include San Diego-Tijuana, El Paso-Cuidad Juarez, Laredo-Nuevo Laredo, Brownsville-

(133)

Matamoros, Vancouver-Victoria-Seattle-Tacoma, Detroit-Windsor, Toronto-Buffalo, and maybe someday, Miami-Havana!

Activity 15

Students' plans should demonstrate a thorough understanding of the material and history of Berlin. Accept all reasonable responses.

Activity 16

1. Answers will vary but students should note the large increases in foreign residents from Central and South America as well as Africa.

2. Autonomous communities with the highest levels of foreign residents are of two kinds, island groups and the autonomous communities with Spain's two largest cities. Island groups (including Spain's "islands" on the African continent) are highly accessible to immigrants (many illegal immigrants come by boat), especially from North Africa, and also offer many jobs in the tourism sector. Madrid and Barcelona offer diverse job opportunities and the largest established communities of foreign residents who act as magnets to others, thus setting up migration chains. The next group includes Andalucia and Valencia, which are coastal, making them easily accessible; also their economies include large labor-intensive agricultural and tourism sectors. Galicia may receive migrants from overseas via its ports and coasts, but also Portuguese from nearby, as the Galicians share their language and other cultural traits with the Portuguese. The more industrialized north of Spain attracts fewer immigrants, who are underrepresented throughout Spain in manufacturing jobs (or at least in non-informal manufacturing jobs). The autonomous communities with the fewest migrants are in Spain's interior, which makes them the least accessible and also less likely to have many jobs in intensive agriculture or tourism (which in Spain is

beach-oriented). They also have few large cities.

Activity 17

1. Northern Dvina, Pechora, Ob'/Irtysh, Yenisey/Angara, Lena, Kolyma
2. Amur
3. Don, Volga, Volgograd
4. Volga
5. Novorossiysk, Kaliningrad, and Murmansk. Even though Novorossiysk itself is ice-free year-round, it is not connected to an ice-free inland waterway system; also use of the Black Sea requires agreement with other nations. Kaliningrad is an exclave of Russia, unconnected to it except by way of other countries. Murmansk is peripheral and in the winter goods cannot reach it via an ice-free waterway, but require a rail trip. (Also, technically, it is not ice-free, but is kept open for about 50 days out of the year by ice-breakers.)
6. St. Petersburg on the Gulf of Finland and Astrakhan on the Caspian Sea
7. The Pechora, Ob', Yenisey, Lena, Kolyma; Novosibirsk, Chita, Yakutsk; Bratsk, Krasnoyarsk, Moscow, Nizhniy Novgorod, Omsk, Samara, Volgograd
8. Massive flooding; permafrost means the floodwaters can't drain into the soil. Huge expanses of overflow persist for months, making transportation difficult and creating vast habitat for mosquitos and other blood-sucking insects.
9. (a) The north west, focused on Moscow; (b) the north east (Eastern Siberia and the northern Far East). Two, the Transiberian Railroad the Baikal-Amur Mainline.
10. Plusses: access to foreign money to help pay for improvements, bettering the economic situations of inland cities through better transportation links, stimulating trade, improving access to waterways in Europe for Russian vessels, reducing pollution by switching from truck transport to shipping; minus: foreign vessels and trading firms capturing a large share of Russian business.

Russia Activity 17

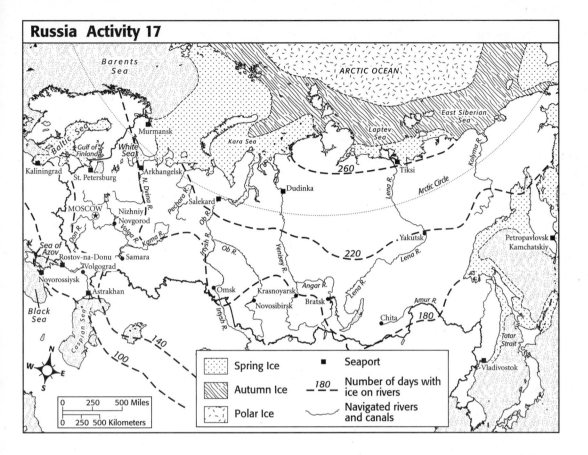

Map legend:
- Spring Ice
- Autumn Ice
- Polar Ice
- Seaport
- 180 — Number of days with ice on rivers
- Navigated rivers and canals

Scale: 0 — 250 — 500 Miles / 0 — 250 — 500 Kilometers

Map labels: Barents Sea, ARCTIC OCEAN, East Siberian Sea, Laptev Sea, Kara Sea, Murmansk, Gulf of Finland, White Sea, Kaliningrad, St. Petersburg, Arkhangelsk, N. Dvina R., Pechora R., Salekard, Ob R., Dudinka, 260, Tiksi, Kolyma R., Arctic Circle, Lena R., MOSCOW, Nizhniy Novgorod, Volga R., Kama R., Irtysh R., Yenisey R., Yakutsk, 220, Lena R., Petropavlovsk Kamchatskiy, Don R., Sea of Azov, Rostov-na-Donu, Samara, Volgograd, Novorossiysk, Astrakhan, Omsk, Krasnoyarsk, Novosibirsk, Bratsk, Angar R., Lena R., Amur R., Chita, 180, Tatar Strait, Black Sea, Caspian Sea, Irtysh R., 140, 100, Vladivostok

Activity 18

1. Students' maps should circle all pertinent locations.
2. Answers will vary but may include some countries in Africa, and India/Pakistan/ Bangladesh.
3. Accept all reasonable responses.
4. Accept all reasonable responses.
5. Accept all reasonable responses.

Activity 19

1. Students maps will vary but should demonstrate the ability to interpret the map appropriately.
2. Answers will vary. Accept all reasonable responses.
3. Answers will vary but may include examples such as conflicts over dam building by a country upstream and how it affects countries downstream and water pollution issues.
4. Answers will vary. Accept all reasonable responses.

5. Answers will vary. Accept all reasonable responses.

Activity 20

Accept all reasonable responses. Students essays should show concerted research and a clear understanding of the site and situation of their chosen city.

Activity 21

1. Egypt
2. Libya
3. Morocco
4. Mexico; Mexico
5. The share of agricultural land irrigated in North Africa is 3.5 times greater than the share of agricultural land irrigated in Africa as a whole and slightly larger than the share of agricultural land irrigated in the world as a whole.
6. Answers should note the relationship between elevation and precipitation and between precipitation and irrigated agricul-

ture. The Nile Valley is low-lying and does not receive much precipitation, but it imports water that fell as precipitation. in another (mountainous) region. Oases are places where underground water comes to the surface as a spring or is near the surface and can be easily lifted. The populations of North African countries are also clustered in the spots where water is available.

7. The water balances are all negative: -1450, -250, -60, -500, -1500. The negative balances mean that the water resource is being depleted and ground water levels are falling.

8. Rates of evaporation in the north are lower than in the south, so the water will "go farther" in the north. Much new infrastructure would have had to have been built in the desert to accommodate farms and people there. People would be reluctant to move from the well-established and climatically milder cities of the north to new desert settlements in the south. The markets, domestic and foreign, are in the north, and it is cheaper to move water there than it would be to move the finished products there.

9. Reduce water consumption by reducing the irrigated area, planting less thirsty crops, use gray water to irrigate forage crops, use drip irrigation and time applications and figure amounts of water more carefully. Use pricing mechanisms to get farmers and other users to conserve. Build more desalinization plants (Libya has plenty of oil to power them, although it does contribute to air pollution and global warming). Develop water projects jointly with neighboring countries. Limit population growth. Abandon the goal of food self-sufficiency. (Does it really make sense to grow low-value crops like wheat or alfalfa in places like Libya, when they can be grown so much more efficiently, in terms of water use, in a more humid environment?)

Activity 22

1.–2. Students maps should accurately plot the various routes on each map.

3. The maps from 1930 and 1950 look most like the "A" network, where the total num-ber of connections between places is limited. The 1975 network is moving toward a "B"-type network, which is achieved by 1984. The 1990s network most resembles network "C."

4. Nigeria is a major oil-producing nation. Its economy prospered with the rising oil prices of the 1970s, and Nigeria enjoyed a period of democratic rule from 1979 to 1984. Geographer Osi Akpoghomeh also points out that the air network's growth phase is associated with an increase in the number of states in Nigeria and the desire to bring air service to all of them. Starting in 1984, there were several military coups; Nigeria suffered (and continues to suffer) from widespread corruption, gross governmental inefficiency, and repression of human rights. Oil prices declined, Nigeria incurred huge foreign debts, inflation was rampant, and international financial institutions demanded reduced government spending as part of structural adjustment programs. Nigeria had the 33rd highest per capita income in the world in the 1970s and it was considered one of Africa's bright stars. By 1997, it was the world's 13th poorest nation (out of about 200). The retrenchment of the 1990s took the form of a shift to a hub-and-spoke system, which allows airlines to keep serving some smaller places, while increasing the likelihood that planes will fly full.

5. Ibadan is a large city of over a million people, but it is close to Lagos and can be reached from there by short automobile or train rides. Kano is much farther away; it is the chief city of northern—Hausa and Fulani—Nigeria; it acts as a sort of secondary hub for that part of the country.

Activity 23

Students presentations should demonstrate a clear understanding of the issues and information.

Activity 24

Students' maps should accurately track the data provided. Answers will vary but should see a relationship between low elevation and infant mortality.

Activity 25

1. Students should accurately categorize states by language.
2. Accept all reasonable responses.
3. Both sides of the debate should present a clear understanding of the pros and cons of each position.

Activity 26

Students' posters should include a map with relevant features. Accept all reasonable responses.

Activity 27

Students' essays should answer all ideas and questions posed. Accept all reasonable responses. The following provinces should be shaded on the map:
.800–.899: Guangdong, Shanghai, Tianjin, and Beijing
.700–.799: Fujian, Zhajian, Jiangsu, Shandong, and Liaoning
.600–.699: Heilongjiang, Jilin, Hebei, Shanxi, Henan, Anhui, Hubei, Guangxi, Hainan, and Xinjiang
.500–.599: Inner Mongolia, Ningxia, Shaanxi, Gansu, Qinghai, Sichuan, Jiangxi, Hunan, Guizhou, and Yunnan
.300–.399: Tibet

Activity 28

Accept all reasonable responses.

Activity 29

1. Students' maps should be shaded according to the appropriate category.
2. Accept all reasonable responses.
3. Accept all reasonable responses.

Activity 30

Accept all reasonable responses.

Activity 31

15 Largest Urban Areas in New Zealand, 2000

1. Auckland. 1,105,700. Chief port of New Zealand (with harbors on both east and west coasts of North Island!). Diversified manufacturing, including dairy products (surrounding farm specialty is dairying), textiles and clothing, chemicals, vehicle assembly. The University of Auckland is located there.
2. Wellington. 346, 500. Capital of New Zealand. Port city (more oriented to coastal shipping than Auckland, which handles a lot of overseas trade) and transportation center. Headquarters for financial, corporate, and many cultural and scientific organizations. Home of Victoria University of Wellington. Diversified manufacturing.
3. Christchurch. 342,000. Largest city on South Island. Manufacturing center, especially transport equipment, carpets, meatpacking, woolens. University of Christchurch. (Nearby Lyttleton serves as its port.)
4. Hamilton. 170,900. Central place and manufacturing center (food processing, agricultural equipment, meat freezing, sawmills, electronics). University of Waikato.
5. Napier-Hastings. 114,500. Port city exporting fruit, wool, frozen meats, dairy products, timber products.
6. Dunedin. 111,700. Manufacturing includes ship repair, brewing, chemicals, furniture. University. Port at Otago exports frozen meat, wool, dairy products.
7. Tuaranga. 94,000. Port specializing in forest product exports.
8. Palmerston North. 75,800. The main town (central place) of a rich farming area. Diversified manufacturing, including processing of local agricultural output. Has an agricultural research center and a university.
9. Rotorua. 54,900. Tourist city and health resort. Hot springs, mud pools, geysers.
10. Nelson. 52,400. Port city on large and sheltered harbor. Timber and fruit and

vegetable processing; tourism in connection with Nelson Lakes National Park.

11. Invercargill. 46,600. Central place for surrounding sheep and dairy-farming region. Manufacturing includes fertilizer and meat-freezing. Port is at Bluff, 15 miles south.

12. New Plymouth. 48,900. Central place for a rich dairy-farming region. Dairy products. Supply base for off-shore Maui gas fields.

13. Whangarei. 47,300. Central place for peninsula north of Auckland. Its port, a fine natural harbor on a deep inlet, serves New Zealand's only oil refinery. Manufacturing.

14. Wanganui. 40,400. Port.

15. Gisborne. 33,100. Seaport and resort. Exports meat, dairy products, wool. Tourists visit forested mountains, including Mt. Hikurangi. First landing site of Captain James Cook in New Zealand (1769).

Activity 32

2. Based on one set of map measurements, the tau for number of species and distance to New Guinea comes out to .87, the same as for number of species and island size. Distance measurements are crude (students are "eyeballing" the centers of island groups) and depend on the map projection used, so answers will differ slightly. Note that map measurements do not have to be converted into miles or kilometers, as all that is needed is relative distances for conversion into ranks. However, teachers may want to have students do the scale conversions just for practice and to get a sense for the scale of the region they are working with.